CHRISTOPHER JONES

Captain of the Mayflower

CHRISTOPHER JONES

CAPTAIN OF THE MAYFLOWER

by ETTA DeGERING

illustrated by William Ferguson

DAVID McKAY COMPANY, Inc.   NEW YORK

Also by Etta DeGering

SEEING FINGERS
The Story of Louis Braille

GALLAUDET
Friend of the Deaf

CHRISTOPHER JONES,
Captain of the *Mayflower*

COPYRIGHT © 1965 BY ETTA DEGERING

LIBRARY OF CONGRESS CATALOG CARD NUMBER: 65-22963

MANUFACTURED IN THE UNITED STATES OF AMERICA
VAN REES PRESS • NEW YORK
Typography by Charles M. Todd

MY SINCERE APPRECIATION to Roger C. Taylor, Editorial Director of the United States Naval Institute, Annapolis, Maryland, for professional guidance in the use of nautical terms pertinent to the *old* ships. Because of Mr. Taylor's help, the square-riggers of this book sailed confidently into Print.

—*Etta DeGering*

FOREWORD

Perhaps no man ever had a more clear cut case for libel suit than Captain Christopher Jones of the *Mayflower*. And had he been alive at the time he might have availed himself of legal action to clear his name. As burgess of Harwich he was familiar with law and courts. In England's Admiralty Records we find him taking advantage of judicial judgment, once to retrieve for his wife, Josian, "furniture and two silver whistles" which had belonged to her late husband, Harold Gray. Again, he is reported suing a man who incited his dog to bite a *May-*

flower apprentice disabling him for work. Still another account records him making legal claim for compensation while the *Mayflower* was held in port during a lawsuit.

For nearly three hundred years, Americans labeled Captain Jones a pirate, an extortioner, a taker of bribes. They identified him as Thomas Jones, highwayman of sea routes. A year after the Pilgrims landed, Thomas Jones called at Plymouth in a ship named *Mayflower* with much needed supplies and charged exhorbitant prices. Out of this grew the extortion charge. Ironically, the captain of the Pilgrim *Mayflower* was in his grave at the time.

The finding of William Mullins' will—the original is now in Somerset House, London—proved conclusively that the captain of the historical ship was Christopher Jones, a mariner and ship builder of repute, not Thomas Jones, a seaman of questionable character. Christopher Jones, along with Dr. Giles Heale and John Carver had signed the shoe merchant's will while the *Mayflower* lay at anchor in Plymouth harbor, New England, 1621.

The Dutch, from whom the *Mayflower* captain was accused of taking a bribe to land the Pilgrims at Cape Cod instead of Dutch territory on the Hudson, cleared him of that charge; instead of trying to prevent, they had tried to persuade the Pilgrims to occupy the southern territory. So, after three centuries of infamy and slander, the man who sacrificed himself and his ship for America, began to come into his rightful place of honor.

Choosing the theme, "America atones, Captain Jones," I began working on the story of Christopher Jones some years ago, proceeding as with an oil painting—first sketching in the bare facts taken from wills, port books, Admiralty reports, and church records. Then dipping my brush into the browns of history, the green-golds of Elizabethan and Stuart customs, and the blue-gray of the sea and ships, I interpreted and rounded out the scene. The foreground was added from the reports of the Pilgrims themselves.

The retouching was done as I sat on Burial Hill, Plymouth, Massachusetts, overlooking Plymouth harbor. On the beach below lies Plymouth Rock. At a nearby pier is moored the *Mayflower II,* "built of the same Devon oak as *Mayflower I,* and presented to America by the British as a good will gesture." Beyond is Gurnet Point where the forefathers' shallop came near disaster, and still beyond, visible on clear days, the arm of Cape Cod, where Christopher Jones first sought shelter for his ship.

I saw the herring *run* in Town Brook, and eels, such as Tisquantum tramped from its mud . . . I visited Pilgrim Hall with its relics of 1620—Peregrine White's cradle, the sword of Miles Standish, Elder Brewster's chair. I took the bus to Plimoth Plantation where Arthur G. Pyle and his colleagues have authentically reproduced the original Leyden Street of the *Mayflower* voyagers. The libraries of both institutions, rich in research, opened wide their doors. But always I came back to Burial Hill to work on the manuscript canvas. And there, on a day reminiscent of that spring more than three hundred years ago when "the birds sang most pleasantly," the word-picture was signed.

The Author

CONTENTS

Contents

CHRISTOPHER JONES

Captain of the Mayflower

1. Eighteen Take Away Eight

SMOTHERY gray fog swirled inland from the North Sea.
It dripped like rain from the high cliffs at the foot
of which nestled the borough of Harwich, England. In
the slate-roof stone house on the high street beside the
River Stour, the three members of the Jones family—
Mistress Sibell Jones, eight-year-old Christopher, and
Roger, six—ate their eleven o'clock meal in silence.
Christopher found it difficult to swallow past the choking
lump in his throat. He could hardly finish his herring
pastie, radishes, and cider.

Always before, as long as he could remember, the
table had been set for four, although oftener than not,
there were only the three of them to eat. Father, for
whom he was named, was a master mariner and absent
for weeks at a time, but Mother insisted, " 'Tis a com-
fortable care for a man at sea to know his porringer and
mug are on ye table 'midst his family." More than once,

1

Father, returning from a voyage, had opened the door on them *at table,* and always his place was waiting for him.

But today, when Christopher came to dinner, there were only three places set—his place was missing. Mother had put her hand on his shoulder, and looked at him a long minute before she spoke. "Christopher, beginning today, you will sit at your father's place. You are now ye head of our family."

Quickly, she had turned to stir the cooking fire that needed no stirring. He knew she did it to hide the tears that wouldn't stay back. Just yesterday, they had buried Father in the graveyard of All Saints Church.

Christopher sat in his father's chair, and said the family grace:

We give thanks to God with one accord
For all that's set upon this board.

But the pastie was as tasteless as wood chips dried in the sun, and the radishes and cider had lost their bite. As soon as he had downed the last mouthful, he asked to be excused. Taking his hooded leather sea jacket from the peg beside the door, and pretending not to hear when Roger asked, "Where be you goin', Chris?" he went out and shut the door behind him.

Slipping into the jacket, he made his way along the narrow stony street to the base of the cliff and climbed to the lookout ledge, where, on clear days the boys and girls of Harwich watched for their fathers' sails. On such days, there would be his friend Richard Gray, whose father was on an exploring expedition in the North Atlantic; lively Josian Thompson, who told of her father's daring as he preyed on enemy treasure ships. They teased her, calling her father a pirate.

"He's *not* a pirate, he's a privateer. Pirates take treasure for themselves. A privateer has a letter from the queen to take treasure for the kingdom." Flashing brown eyes dared them to dispute her.

Sarah Twitt usually came but never talked much. Her father sailed whalers up Iceland way. Christopher's father had commanded *The Centurion* and the *Marie Fortune,* merchant ships, carrying cargo to and from England and the Continent.

No one would be on the lookout today. Christopher was glad for the fog. He wanted to be alone. He pushed back his sea hood to get the full feel of wet fog against his face. He liked the smell it brought—the mixed-up smell of seaweed and fish, of newly-tarred ships' hulls, of driftwood and hemp.

Against the tumbling roar of the sea, he could hear the trumpets and drums of ships warning each other of their presence as they waited for the fog to lift to enter the harbor. Each ship had its own trumpet sound or drum beat. The watchman on The Andrews sand bank tolled a steady "bong . . . bong . . . bong." Night and day, he kept a coal fire burning behind a huge iron grate.

Christopher looked above him. He could barely make out Paine's tree on Beacon Hill. On fair days and moonlight nights, captains ranged on the elm to guide their ships into Harwich harbor; a fine deep harbor it was, carved out by the Stour and Orwell rivers as they met and flowed into the North Sea. Christopher knew every curve of it. He knew every ship's berth.

It was there on the ledge with Richard, Josian, and Sarah, the last day of last May, that he had gotten an idea. The four of them had climbed to the lookout to watch Captain Sir Martin Frobisher's fleet of fifteen ships as it made ready to begin Sir Martin Frobisher's third voyage in search of a northwest passage to Cathay and India. The fleet carried people and supplies to plant a colony for her Majesty, Queen Elizabeth, in the New World. The ships had left London the day before, but stopped in Harwich harbor to take on a further supply of victuals.

Josian excitedly told about Queen Elizabeth's London farewell to the captains of the fleet. Her father had told her. "The queen hung a wondrous gold chain around Captain Frobisher's neck," she said. "And all of the captains kissed her jeweled hand—all fifteen of them!"

Richard took no notice. His whole attention was down there in the harbor with the *Anne Francis,* in which his father was sailing as first mate.

"What's so ruddy special about hand-kissing?" Christopher wanted to know.

Josian had stamped her foot and glared at him. "Why, why, you ignorant boy! It's the most beautiful custom in all England!"

"Not so," he had hotly denied. "Down there in the harbor is the most beautiful custom in all England!"

The fifteen captains, wearing uniforms of green and white with starched ruffs, and plumed hats of black and gold, stood, each on his ship's poop deck, barking final commands. Silver trumpets blared. Sails burst out in a blizzard of white and dingy gray. The ships' guns gave a final earthshaking salute. When the smoke had cleared, there was the fleet sailing out of Harwich harbor as gracefully and silently as swans, the *Aide*, Sir Martin Frobisher's flagship, leading, the *Anne Francis* fourth in line.

Every day, since that last day of May, Christopher had imagined himself a Captain Frobisher commanding a fleet bound for the New World. Every time he thought of it, a shivery tingle ran up his back and spread through him even to the tips of his fingers and toes. But today, he was pretty sure that such an adventure wasn't for him—might as well dunk the idea into the harbor. He couldn't go adventuring. He was head of a family. He would sail ships, of course, but in a steady line of work. Like his father, he would be a merchant mariner, carry cargoes of wool and calfskins to the Continent, and there load his ship with bags of salt, casks of wine, and various things for other ports.

A fortnight or so after that foggy morning, the executor of the late Captain Christopher Jones's will knocked on the oak door of the stone house beside the Stour. He had come, he said, to read the deceased captain's will to the family. Christopher's mother invited him in, giving him Father's chair beside the open fire. She indicated a bench for the boys, and took her place on the carved settle opposite the man.

Christopher sat very straight as he thought the head of

5

a family should. Roger had no such responsibility. He swung his feet back and forth and fidgeted.

The executor unfolded the crackly parchment, blew his nose noisily on a black-bordered kerchief, sighed as if the task were not to his liking, and began to read.

October 13, 1578—Christopher Jones, mariner, being sick of bodie, but sound of mind, doth hereby make his last will and testament ... To my wife, Sibell Jones, my house in the high street at Harwich next to the water, with the keye, and all appurtenances to same, together with all implements and household stuff in same, for life, and afterwards equally among my children. To my youngest son, Roger Jones, and to a child yet unborn, all that my

eight parte and stocke of the new ship called The
Centurion, to be equally divided betwixt them.

So Roger was to have Father's "eight parte" in *The*
Centurion, but who was that child that was to share it
with him—that "child yet unborn?" Was mother going
to have a baby? Another boy? Christopher felt a queer
feeling inside him. What if it were a girl?

The next part of the will was about money his father
had left to the poor of Harwich, payable at the Feast of
the Nativity. Father was like that, kind to poor folk,
especially to the children of seamen who were not lucky
enough to "come back."

The executor read on:

Also I give my parte of the ship called the Marie
Fortune, with the stock belonging to same, to my
eldest son, Christopher Jones, at 18 years . . .

He was a ship owner! The *Marie Fortune* was his!
Well—it would be when he was eighteen. How long
would he have to wait? Eight plus what made eighteen?
He was sure the answer was ten.

The executor was on his third mug of cider. How
slowly he drank! Surely he wouldn't take a fourth. Christopher wiggled his toes back and forth in his boots. He
wished the man would go. There was a question he
wanted to ask Mother, something he wanted to check.

Finally, the executor stood up. He shook hands with
Mother, with Roger, and then with him. "Be obedient
sons," he said, "and help your mother as your dear,
departed father would wish you to." With his hand on the

doorknob, he turned back. "Remember," he cautioned, accenting the words with a wagging finger that almost touched Christopher's nose, " 'Idle hands are a predilection of Satan.' "

Christopher looked at his hands. He wondered what "predilection" meant. A sickness, maybe. Anyway, he didn't have to worry. He wouldn't catch it; his hands wouldn't be idle.

At last the door closed on the executor's back.

"Mother?"

"Yes, Christopher?"

"How much is eighteen, take away eight?"

2. From Ratlines to Rating

CHRISTOPHER lay on the bare forecastle planking trying to adjust himself to the roll of the ship. Sleep
seemed as far away as his featherbed in Harwich. He was
eleven, almost twelve, and apprenticed for seven years
to the master of the *Swallow,* a snub-nosed, two-masted,
crank little merchant vessel, as unswallowlike as a fat
duck.

Three hours ago, he had said good-bye to his mother,
Roger, and three-year-old Grace (the baby had been a
girl), and carried his sea chest on board the *Swallow.* The
ship had put to sea on the ebb tide, under a full moon.

As always, before beginning a voyage, the captain had
called his seamen on deck while he and the pilot chose
them into starboard and larboard watches. Christopher
had drawn larboard. Starboard was first on, but in four
hours the bosun's shrill whistle would call the larboard
up (4 o'clock) to take over the work of the ship. The

9

Swallow provided sleeping accommodations for officers only. Seamen bunked or rather "planked" down in any likely spot where they could brace themselves against the roll and pitch of the ship—in the forecastle, hold, or on deck if weather permitted. No one undressed.

Christopher had made himself as small as possible in a corner of the forecastle. His hip ached from the unaccustomed hardness of the plank floor. He shifted position to relieve it. But the ache-for-home in his chest hurt worse, and no shifting of any kind lessened it.

"You no can sleep?" inquired a voice blurred with sleep and the speech of North England.

The voice belonged to big Jolin "Jon" Stanten, an apprentice in his sixth year. " 'Twon't be long till you can sleep like a 'orse, a-standin' up."

"I—I was wondering what a prentice does to get started."

"Does what 'e's told and does it quick. Then 'twon't be quick enough to suit ye bosun. Like as not," continued Jon, "you'll begin with the 'our glass. Most prentices do. Next you'll learn a ship's parts, box the compass —learn its thirty-two points, climb ratlines, and later, take a turn at the whipstaff. A whipstaff is a wooden staff the helmsman has always in his hand to keep the ship on course. It is fastened to the tiller which turns the rudder from side to side."

Jon yawned. "And you'll do errands for the men above you, and they're all above a grummet, a beginner."

The voice showed that sleep was getting the better of it, and then roused. "An' there'll be whuppins. No sailor is made without help of ye *cat*. Monday is whuppin day for pren-ti-ces." Words trailed into snores.

Christopher thought over what he had just heard. He knew a ship's parts from rudder to rigging. Seemed like he'd been born knowing them. Jon didn't have to explain a whipstaff to him. Climb ratlines? He and Richard had climbed ratlines since they were six; played catch-me-if-you-can over a ship's spars and down backstays. Of course that had been on a ship lying to her anchor. He looked forward to the challenge on the open sea.

But about whuppins—he sighed. If only Solomon, wisest man that ever lived, so his mother said, hadn't written those seven words, "Spare the rod and spoil the child." And everybody read the words differently. The "rod" to his father had meant a strap that hung handy beside the fireplace chimney. Schoolmaster Higgins read the words, "Spare the cane and spoil the scholar." And now the seven words had followed him on ship, and they read, "Spare the cat and spoil the sailor." But the cat didn't have nine tails like the one used in the navy, thank be. It was a single rope with a clout in the end.

Christopher finally slept. He dreamed that he was in the ship's swaying maintop, and he had fallen asleep on watch. The bosun, roaring from the deck below, waited for him with a cat-o'-nine-tails as huge as a full grown octopus.

The bosun *was* roaring at him, shaking him. "Think you can sleep all day, you landlubber grummet?"

"I'm sorry, Sir. I . . ."

"Choke the luff, you'll be sorrier come Monday."

As Jon had said, his first job was the hour glass, really

11

a half-hour measure of time—the ship's clock. He tipped the glass, and when the sand had run out, struck the ship's bell above his head—one bell. Again he tipped the glass—two bells, and so on until eight bells or four hours. The starboard watch then took over while the larboard went below to eat, sleep, or pass the time swapping tales of other voyages.

If the ship's hour-glass clock lost or gained time, due to the sand running irregularly during a rough sea or the grummet being slow in reversing the glass, it could be corrected on a sunny day. The captain would place a pin in the center of the ship's compass card about mid-day. When the sun cast the pin's shadow on the exact point of north (12 o'clock) the glass would be turned on a fresh start.

Christopher's work wasn't all "hour glass." He scrubbed decks with a coarse broom and salt water drawn up from the sea in buckets. He scraped and painted bulwarks and hatches, tarred ropes, unraveled old rope for caulking material, and did the everlasting errands of the men before the mast. He was sure they made up jobs just to have somebody to boss and order around.

Everything went fairly well during the week except for the homesickness, the diet of "salt horse"—stringy salt beef or pork served in a common wooden bowl—which he had to make himself eat, and the nagging memory of the bosun's threat. Maybe he would be let off since the misconduct happened on his first day and was his first offense.

But no such luck. Come Monday, the bosun had his fun. The other apprentices howled lustily. Nobody'll ever hear a Jones whimper, Christopher vowed. And nobody did. But he got three lashes to the other fellows' one.

Big Jon tipped him off. "Next time 'owl and save your 'ide."

It was in the rigging, after he had become one of the younkers—the lads who take in topsails, furl and sling the lower sails—that Christopher experienced his first bout with the North Sea. A sudden gale roared out of the northeast, a full-fledged nor'easter.

"All hands!" bellowed the captain. "Furl all! Aloft and furl! . . . Larboard on fores'l . . ."

Catfooted, the larboard younkers swarmed up the foremast ratlines, hands keeping out of way of boots above. Clinging to the careening yard as if frozen to it, they fought the thundering canvas. The sail fought back like a thing alive. The ship pitched, lurched, staggered. The horizon was sometimes far above them, sometimes far beneath. The wind shrieked, clutched at them with icicle fingers, blinded them with sleet. Waves of black water, foaming angry, broke across the deck below. "This can't be real," Christopher told himself. "Must be a nightmare."

When the last foot of sail had been made fast with ropes to the yard, and Christopher was again in the forecastle's shelter, he felt the thrill of his life. He had fought the sea and scored! He forgot the paralyzing cold, forgot the terror he had felt up there on the flailing yard. No matter the bosun roared, called them creeping caterpillars, said the sea was no place for molly-coddling softies. Christopher knew he was but sounding off. Besides, big Jon mumbled in his ear, "Couldn't a-done better m'self."

Before the gale had blown itself out, he knew the meaning of "sleep like a 'orse a-standin' up." He hadn't had his wet clothes off for most a week. He scarcely snatched a wink until "All hands," on the next tack.

Weeks, months, years went by like waves marching across the sea, sometimes gently as before "a faire breeze," sometimes rough and mountainous as in a "blow," but always marching. Christopher became a *sailor* which meant he had learned all there was to learn before the mast. Then he rose to the position of *pilot*. To be a pilot one must know navigation, be able to figure latitudes, identify landmarks, sea lanes, harbors; he must be able to boss a

14

crew. Finally he became *mate,* second only to the captain.

He studied books of rules for seafaring men, charts of new shores, and reports of men who had voyaged far— Sir Martin Frobisher, whose search for a northwest passage to Cathay had not been successful, but who was considered a great seaman no less; Sir Francis Drake who had sailed England's flag around the world; Sir Walter Raleigh and his fleet to the Carolinas. The adventuring idea that Christopher had dunked into the harbor had not drowned. It still came back to invade his dreams and prickle his spine.

At last, in the year 1588, Christopher stood on the deck of the *Marie Fortune,* captain of his own ship—a captain who seamen said had "come up through the hawse hole," meaning by way of apprenticeship and knew all the ropes. He was just in time to do his bit for England in her combat with the *Invincible Armada.*

Queen Elizabeth needed two types of fleets to meet the Spanish-Portuguese aggression, the navy to carry on active warfare, the merchant fleet to keep supplies running. Many merchant ships were being fitted with extra guns to join the regular line of battleships. Was there a chance that the *Marie Fortune* might be drafted? Christopher thought not. Her captain needed to grow apace both in years and experience. He would have to content himself as a part of the merchant fleet.

It was hard to turn his back on the excitement of threatened invasion, and do such a dull thing as sail up coast for a cargo of fish, but sail he must. On his return, less than a fortnight later, he learned there had been a running fight in the Channel between the Spanish Armada and the English navy, that both fleets were then lying-to off Calais.

Scarcely had Christopher unloaded his cargo, when the bells of Harwich began their day-long clanging of victory. A swift pinnace had slipped into harbor with the news that English fire boats had routed the Spanish, that a decisive battle had been fought at Gravelines where Spanish scuppers ran red with blood, that the great Armada was now in flight northward in the North Sea.

All of the merchantmen of Harwich harbor put to sea, perchance they might be of assistance to the navy. Christopher looked to the east and saw the huge castle-like Spanish galleons fleeing past Harwich well offshore, with the smaller but swifter ships of the queen's navy following close on their heels. The flagship *Ark Royal,* commanded by Admiral Lord Howard, and the *Revenge* by Vice-Admiral Sir Francis Drake, led the pursuit. Christopher felt his scalp prickle with pride knowing that both ships were skippered by Harwich men—Thomas Gray, the *Ark Royal,* and Richard's father, John Gray, the *Revenge.*

A signal from the flagship! What did it mean? Christopher shaded his eyes. She was signaling the east coast merchantmen into line! Christopher, his heart pounding, brought the *Marie Fortune* into formation. Some of the regular ships were dropping out for repairs and a desperate bid for food and ammunition.

The English were out of ammunition, but no matter if they could bluff with numbers and keep the Armada moving north. They knew something the Spanish did not— that the North Sea was probably bluffing also, that it was luring the great ships with a "faire south breeze" until they were in its lair, and then it would stand up, join forces with the North Atlantic, and lash them into kindling wood on the lee shores of the Orkneys, Scotland, and Ireland.

At the Firth of Forth the English fleet turned back and let the North Sea take over. Christopher learned later that few more than half of the Armada's ships, and only a third of her men reached the home shores of Spain and Portugal. The English lost no ships and less than a hundred men—an almost unbelievable victory—and the *Marie Fortune* and her captain had had a part, small part though it was.

Queen Elizabeth proclaimed a day of prayer and thanksgiving. England was no longer under the heel of Spain. But the war debt must be paid. From the throne came the urgent orders:

To Sir Francis Drake—"Lead your privateers (that included Josian's father) against the treasure ships of Spain and Portugal. Make them pay the cost of the war for which they are responsible. We shall not tax our people. We shall tax our enemies."

To the merchant fleet—"Keep England's trade moving. England's prosperity depends on her trade."

Christopher rallied to the queen's call. He sailed the *Marie Fortune* with a cargo of wool out of Harwich harbor for the trade centers of Europe, not knowing when he would be in the home port again.

3. "... and in His Heart ..."

IT WAS an August evening, 1592, and already growing
dusk, when Christopher warped the *Marie Fortune*
into Harwich harbor after an absence of three, almost
four years. It was good to see the old familiar landmarks.
The fire on The Andrews sand bank glowed its orange
of warning and welcome. Paine's tree on Beacon Hill,
that had guided generations of his ancestor-mariners into
port, appeared this evening to have been cut from black
paper and pasted against the dimming sky.

But what was going on in the home borough? A festi-
val? A fair? Flares lighted crowded streets and water-
front decorated with flags. There was the sound of music,
of jollity. Then he saw that the center of the fanfare was
a ship moored to the wharf. The vessel was bedecked
with pennons, banners, and rich cloth as was the custom

of ships celebrating a triumph. He tried to read the scarred name on her stern, visible between the swallow tails of a banner that stretched from maintop to waterline, but couldn't make it out.

Hardly had the *Marie Fortune* nudged the wharf when her crew, Harwich men and boys, went over her side, drawn like gnats to the lights. They were loudly glad to be home.

It was then that Christopher took note of the ship on his larboard. *The Centurion!* He was in luck! Roger was in port.

Ashore, he made his way along the wharf towards the gayly decorated ship. The *Dainty!* Huh, she didn't look her name with makeshift mast, battered rails, and patched hull that showed in spite of all the trappings. Must have been in some ruddy fight. He knew England's ships. The *Dainty* belonged to Richard Hawkins, son of Sir John Hawkins, administrator of the queen's navy. But what was she doing here? Who was sailing her? Why the battle wounds?

"Who's her master?" he asked the dock night watch who tramped the pier, glowering at the crowds.

"Capt'n Thomas Thompson ... sir," the tardy "sir" after he had taken note of his questioner's obvious rank. "The *Dainty,* she helped capture ye treasure ship, *Madre de Dios*. Already for two days, the music"—he spat— "the crowd."

So Josian's father was in port, and a hero. Christopher smiled, remembering how a small girl's brown eyes had snapped as she tried to convince her tormentors, "He's *not* a pirate, he's a privateer." Well, he would first go

19

home and see how his mother, Grace, and Roger fared, and then go meet the celebrated privateer. Perchance, the privateer's daughter might be present also.

Christopher pulled the latchstring of the stone house on the Stour, and paused in the doorway. His surprised mother quickly put down her wool carder and came to meet him. "My family all home together!" she cried. "My cup runneth over. Surely . . ." She couldn't finish the Psalm. Mother always wept when her boys came home —for joy, she said.

He led her back to her chair. "Where are Grace and Roger?"

"They attend ye celebration. Hast not heard about ye treasure ship, greatest ever taken?"

He assured her he had, and would soon be joining ye merry-making. "But Grace, is she old enough for such?"

Sibell Jones laughed. "You are gone a long time. Your little sister grows up. Besides, Roger is with her."

On his way to join his brother and sister at the *Dainty,* Christopher stopped aboard the *Marie Fortune* to change clothes. He donned his best silk stockings, white breeches, scarlet velvet jerkin with brass buttons, and a crisply starched ruff; he buckled on his best sword.

Josian, dressed in a farthingale of yellow silk brocade, stood in the ship's receiving line with citizens of Harwich welcoming guests. Christopher thought—she's as beautiful as a sun goddess. He bowed low and kissed the hand she held out to him. "The most beautiful custom in all England," he murmured. They laughed together, remembering.

He moved on to the group gathered about Captain

Thompson. There, he found Roger and Grace. Was this young lady with fan and gracious manners the sister who, but a few summers ago, challenged him at rowing? Girls, it seemed, could change as unexpectedly as the sea. He was pleased to find Sarah Twitt and her brother Michael with them. Sarah wore a dress of brown velvet which suited her quiet manner.

Someone clapped him on the back. "Richard Gray! Of all . . ."

Captain Thompson came forward. "If the young captains and their friends will come to the great cabin, it would give me much pleasure to personally tell them of the capture of the *Madre de Dios.*"

The group followed the captain to the great cabin where was displayed a sampling of the contraband taken by his men—silks, Chinese porcelains, ebony, amber, and musk. The heavy fragrance of musk filled the cabin.

"The men who stormed the ship," he reminded them, "are entitled to the booty of the orlop (lowest deck)." His eyes twinkled as he touched some of the more exquisite pieces. "I fear some seamen have difficulty in distinguishing the orlop from other decks."

Vessels of the queen's fleet, he explained, had lain in wait near the Azores most a fortnight, watching for certain Portuguese treasure ships reported homeward bound from Cathay. He of the *Dainty* had been first to espy the 1600-ton carrack, *Madre de Dios,* looming up over the horizon. "The *Dainty,*" the captain spoke her name with pride, "being of excellent sail, got start of the rest of the fleet and began the conflict. Cannon blazed on both sides." He paused and shook his head. "There was much damage to the ship and many men wounded before the remainder of the fleet moved in."

Then had come the boarding, when men fell upon each other with "clash of cutlass and push of pike." The Portuguese fought valiantly but were finally overpowered; their captain and crew were placed into a well-provisioned boat and dismissed to their own country. The treasure—seven decks of wealth—was taken in the name of England's queen. Such treasure no one had ever before seen. There were spices, three hundred and seventy tons of pepper alone, valued at ninety thousand pounds, damasks, silks, oriental rugs, elephants' tusks, rubies, diamonds, strands of pearls . . .

Christopher privately wondered if the cost of the Armada conflict had not now been met. But it would be poor taste to interrupt with so practical a question on so splendid an occasion.

The *Dainty's* foremast and bowsprit had been badly splintered, and when the wind came up both had crashed into the sea. Captain Thompson made a wry face. "She drifted aimlessly while I labored to fit her out with jury masts. By the time I could board the treasure ship, there was no treasure left, not even a chain of gold for around my neck."

"But I have heard," said Richard Gray, "that there is something better in store for the captain than a chain of gold."

"And what, pray, hast thou heard, young man?"

"It is voiced everywhere, that the queen plans to appoint Captain Thompson one of the Principal Masters in her navy for his valor in the capture of the *Madre de Dios.*"

The captain looked pleased. "Come, we shall go out on the ship's deck for refreshments. I regret that my daughter is occupied and cannot join us." He is not alone in his regrets, thought Christopher.

As they ate cakes and drank cordials, Christopher found himself telling Sarah all that had happened to him during the past four years. It was easy to talk to Sarah. Strange he had never noticed it before.

While in harbor, the three captains readied their ships

against the next sail. They hove them down on a sandy beach, scraped barnacles and sea growth from their hulls, and then daubed them with a mixture of pitch and tallow to discourage teredo worms which liked nothing better than a diet of oak planking. They tarred their ship's standing rigging, the lines that held the masts in place. They inspected their running rigging, the lines by which sails and spars were adjusted. Both were made of hemp rope, and subject to chafe and wear.

For old times' sake, they climbed the cliff with Josian and Sarah, Sarah's brother Michael and Grace now included. They picnicked on Beacon Hill, went on moonlight excursions, chaperoned of course, up the Orwell.

Then came the Monday, when at daybreak, Christopher stood on the deck of the *Marie Fortune,* weighed anchor, and sailed out of Harwich harbor. On board, he carried a Harwich crew; in the hold, bales of wool; and in his heart, the promise of Sarah to become his wife.

The records of All Saints Church show that in the year of 1593, Christopher Jones married Sarah Twitt. Richard Gray married Josian Thompson. Christopher brought his bride home to the stone house on the high street beside the River Stour. The house seemed pleased with the arrangement.

Perhaps his marrying a whaler's daughter had something to do with his next venture. A great herd of whales was reported off Greenland shores. Christopher filled the hold of the *Marie Fortune* with casks for blubber, with harpoons, lances, and flenching knives, and sailed with a whaling fleet for Greenland. He leaves no record of his whaling experiences. Months later, when he returned home, he presented Sarah with a splendid sum from the sale of whale oil; she presented him with a son.

They named the baby Thomas after Sarah's father, Thomas Twitt. Again, head of a family, Christopher settled down to the work of merchant mariner. A son gave double meaning to his homecomings, a double welcome. He looked forward to the day when he could teach him the ways of a ship. But this was not to be.

A fever took small Thomas from them. Seven years later, Sarah died after a lingering illness, as quietly as she had lived. Now Sarah and son Thomas were together in All Saints churchyard. Christopher was alone. The night after burying Sarah, he climbed the cliff to gather strength from the expanse of sky and its host, but clouds were all that he could see.

Ill fortune did not end there. His friend, Richard Gray, passed away. And on a bleak windy March day (1603), at two-thirty in the afternoon, Queen Elizabeth, Good Queen Bess, her subjects called her, breathed her last after a reign of forty-five years.

Christopher turned the key in the heavy oak door of the stone house beside the Stour on an empty home. (His mother had long since re-married. Grace had married Michael Twitt and moved to a home of her own, as had Roger.) He sailed the *Marie Fortune* to France for a cargo of wine. He was desolate! England was desolate!

4. Burgess and Shipbuilder

SOME months later, Christopher delivered a cargo of wine in Southampton, then returned to Harwich—his mind made up. He was annoyed that a dense fog blanketed the harbor. He could either wait for the fog to lift or feel his way in with soundings. He decided not to wait.

The *Marie Fortune* moved cautiously under shortened sail; her leadsman chanting depth; her captain barking orders to the helmsman below; boatswain blowing a nearly continuous trumpet warning. And then, with a great splash, her anchor dove into the harbor and bit into its mud. She was deserted by crew and captain, everyone except the watch.

Christopher made his way resolutely along the narrow

street, not to the stone house on the Stour, but to the home
of the young widow, Josian Thompson-Gray. Josian herself answered the knock. She did not seem surprised to
see him. He found himself bowing formally, even stiffly,
as he kissed her proffered fingertips.

A mug of mulled cider, spiced with cinnamon and
ginger, was cheering after the raw morning and helped
to relieve a strained tension, a tension he had never before felt in Josian's presence. When youngsters they had
climbed the cliff together. He had pulled her brown
braids. She had boxed him soundly on the ears. Why
this strangeness? He had a feeling she was laughing at
him behind her polite smile.

She spoke of the latest happenings in Harwich. He
told her of grape vineyards under blue skies. They talked
of King James I, the new king on England's throne, and
what his rule might mean to England. And then Christopher remembered something that had puzzled him.

"You didn't seem surprised to see me this morning."

Josian laughed. "I heard your trumpet. It gives warning not only to ships, but to others."

"You know the voice of my ship's trumpet?" he asked
hopefully.

Did a guilty look steal across Josian's face? "I know
many ships' trumpets," she countered.

Christopher knelt before her. He took her hand and
again kissed its fingertips—this time with a proposal of
marriage.

The stone house on the high street beside the River Stour
echoed with Josian's laughter. The new housewife was

determined that Christopher's and her life together should be as solid as its stone walls.

She stood her chair beside the fireplace opposite Christopher's chair, the one that had been his father's. She placed new coverlets and canopies on the beds, and bleached calico curtains at the windows. She hummed a tune as she rolled out a baking of current tarts. Christopher would show his appreciation by the number he ate, or he might say, "These biscuits are ruddy special."

People said her man had an iron jaw, an iron fist. Both were necessary to a captain of the sea, but she always looked at his eyes. They were kind eyes that smiled even when his mouth didn't. Already, at thirty-three, he was getting wrinkles at their corners from squinting latitudes with the cross-staff.

Shortly after marriage, Christopher was honored with the position of Burgess of Harwich. King James I had granted a charter to the borough, naming a politic body of twenty-four burgesses who would have all of the authority of the old manor lord, and who would elect two members to parliament each year. At home after the ceremony, Josian curtsied, "My Lord Burgess."

"My Lady Burgess," Christopher responded with proper deference.

Christopher decided it was high time he had a new ship, that he would build the ship himself. He rented a berth in a nearby shipyard, and laid the keel for a two hundred and forty-ton-burthen ship. The same number of well-seasoned oaks would be required for its building. Those for the ribs of the ship must be sought that had grown with proper curve. The north wind, Christopher mused, that curves oaks into ships' ribs, is at the same time unwittingly shaping them to resist its fury at sea. Of an evening Josian came down to see how the ship progressed, and to smell the pitchy fragrance of new wood. They walked home together.

One evening, the day he had fashioned the binnacle, she didn't come. He walked home alone. When he had closed the oak door behind him, Josian's mother came forward with a bundle of swaddling clothes which she placed in his arms. A faint mewling came from within. "Meet your new son, Captain Jones," she said.

With both love and fear clutching his heart, he carried the bundle to the bedroom. How was Josian after her ordeal? To his relief, he found that her brown eyes still sparkled, though tiredly.

"What shall we name him?" she whispered.

"You name the baby," he said, "I'll name the ship."

"I would like to name him Thomas after my father." Josian closed her eyes. "He would consider a namesake-grandson a greater treasure than the treasures of the *Madre de Dios.*"

Christopher winced. " 'Tis a good English name," he said aloud, but inwardly he prayed that heaven would be more merciful to this wee Thomas than that other one he had known such a short time.

"What will you name the ship?" Josian asked.

"You must wait. It is bad luck to tell a ship's name before the christening."

Weeks later, Josian wrapped baby Thomas, against her mother's protest, for a trip to the shipyard. "A son must be present at his father's launching," she stoutly declared.

Holding the shawled bundle, she stood beside Christopher at the ship's prow during the speeches and prayer. He then held the chalice of wine aloft, and announced, "I christen thee *Josian of Harwich*."

Josian gasped. "Oh Christopher, how nice!" she whispered.

Christopher then dropped the chalice into the harbor. A boy swam to retrieve it, completing the ceremony of christening a ship in the style of 1606.

The ship brought Christopher another honor. King James wrote his exchequer that among vessels built by "well-beloved subjects . . . at their costs and charges, and to the increase of our navy of this realm was one *Josian of Harwich,* built by a burgess of the king's appointment, Christopher Jones." He granted that "for every ton burden of the said ship, one crown of the double rose . . . be granted Master Jones."

Christopher was pleased and he was *not* pleased. "Far better the king build some ships of his own," he told Josian. "Since Queen Elizabeth, the navy has gone down until I doubt even the teredo worms are interested in it." Josian glanced toward the door and lowered her voice. "I hear that the king is puffed up in both body and office. They say his spindly legs can hardly bear him up; that his eyes are puffed, and his lips so puffed that they never quite cover his teeth. Do you suppose he has the water-sickness?"

"I know not," said Christopher, "but as to office, King James believes in the divine right of kings, that he has been appointed by a higher power and is accountable to no man."

Christopher and Josian sat before the fire and gravely spoke of the religious troubles in England since the king's inauguration. Queen Elizabeth had been strict, making non-attendance at church a matter of severe punishment, but her subjects were allowed to attend the church of their choice, whether Catholic, Puritan, Separatist, or State Church. She would not allow herself to be called the head of the church. "I desire to open the window on no man's conscience," she had said.

But King James claimed that as king he was head of the church as well as the realm. He decreed that all subjects must attend the State Church under penalty of imprisonment or death. "I will *make* them conform," he had bellowed, "or harry them out of the kingdom." And therein lay the greater trouble—when subjects wished to leave England that they might have freedom of worship in some other country, he would not permit them to go. Many were thrown into dark dank prisons, others put to death as examples. Still, many attempted to flee rather than give up their beliefs.

A Dutch captain had told Christopher of picking up a group of Separatists—so named because they wished to separate from the State Church—on a deserted coast north of Harwich from under the nose of a mob armed with pikes and guns swooping down on his ship. The captain had been greatly impressed by one of the men, a William Brewster, former postmaster of Scrooby, and a Cambridge graduate who had been in the queen's employ. But the name was just a name to Christopher.

The fire in the grate burned low. It was late and Christopher must leave in the morning. He stood up and stretched. "A sea captain hasn't much worry about state and church affairs; he is king of his ship at sea. But a sea captain's wife"—Christopher looked earnestly at Josian—"had best not talk about the king nor things pertaining to church and state when speaking with her neighbors. It is not a healthy nor safe conversation."

"I will obey my husband," promised Josian. "While he is away, I'll think and talk about the weaving that must be done—we need yards of cloth—about how the wee one grows, and about when my captain's ship will be coming home."

5. A Ruddy Ship

A THREE-MASTED square rigger came in from sea and beat up into Harwich harbor. The westering sun turned her canvas into cloth-of-gold, and lit her cabin windows with a thousand candles.

"Right purty, think ye?" commented a grizzled barge captain who stood on the wharf with Christopher watching the ship come in.

"Right purty," Christopher echoed the captain's words. "A ruddy ship if ever I saw one—a ruddy ship."

" 'Tis ye *Mayflower of London*," the older man informed him. "The very same as was anchored off Gravesend a fortnight ago when I was unloadin' coal there. I hear tell she's a-biddin' for ye fourth owner and captain."

The "ruddy ship" sailed right into Christopher's heart and life. Before many hours he was fourth owner and captain of the *Mayflower*. Whether he traded his share in the *Josian* for that in the other ship, or bought her outright, he leaves no record. But from then on, in port books his name is linked with the *Mayflower*.

Christopher swung two-year-old Thomas to his shoulder, and took Josian to see the new ship. He pointed out the graceful lines of her hull. He reeled off dimensions: "keel, sixty-four feet; beam, twenty-six; from beak to taffrail, one hundred and thirteen."

The *Mayflower*, seeming to enjoy the attention, rolled lazily to the harbor surge, ripples lapping at her sides, rigging sighing contentedly in the light breeze. From her mainmast fluttered Britain's Union flag, the red cross of England's Saint George imposed upon the blue cross of Scotland's Saint Andrew. "She carries five hundred and twenty-five yards of canvas," said Christopher, trying to give an idea of the extent of her sail, now harbor-furled. He indicated the bowsprit leaning jauntily forward under which hung a yard with its furled spritsail. "A handy sail to box her about and a good puller before a fair breeze, but not so good in a rough sea; then it's mostly under water."

Mast by mast, Christopher went over the sailing power of the ship—foremast with fore course and fore topsail, mainmast with main course and main topsail, mizzenmast with its yard leaning aft and rigged with a three-cornered lateen sail. "A good pusher," Christopher commented, "and good to keep her on the wind when the wind is contrary." He explained how small extension sails, called bonnets, could be quickly laced to the regular sails for more speed. "She's supposed to do seven knots when weather, wind, and current are favorable."

Christopher and Josian went on board. They placed small Tommy in the longboat lashed to the deck, much to the youngster's delight. There, he would be safely corralled while they explored the high forecastle and the still higher sterncastle. Josian was interested in the cooking arrangement which was simple indeed, a brick box forward partly filled with sand on which the cook would build his wood fire.

High under the poop deck was the captain's cabin opening onto the quarter-deck. From the quarter-deck the pilot would direct the ship by shouting orders through a speaking hatch to the helmsman below who steered with a whipstaff.

Christopher took Josian down to the 'tween deck, warning her to be careful of the ship's beams as there was not head room.

"Twelve guns!" Josian gasped. "Is it that dangerous at sea?"

Christopher laughed. "The more guns, the safer the voyage. When a pirate sees the *Mayflower's* guns he'll turn tail and run."

Josian sniffed the air. "Smells good down here."

Christopher was pleased. "The *Mayflower* is a *sweet ship* from hauling wine. Betimes the wine splashes from the casks and sweetens the evil smell of the bilge." He thumped a seam in the ship's side. "Only tight ships are hired in the wine trade."

If Josian felt jealous because another ship had replaced the one named for her, she said nothing. After all, ships were men's business.

Christopher took the *Mayflower* for a trial run in the Bay of Biscay in August (1609) carrying a cargo of Gascon wine. In the same month he pitted the ship against the North Sea, sailing with a mixed cargo of hats, hops, and Spanish salt to Trondhjem, Norway. The voyage north was without incident. There, he took on a return cargo of herring, deals, and barrels of tar.

As he sailed for home, the North Sea, with gray-flecked eye took notice of the new ship, turned sullen, and whipped up a gale contesting ownership. The sea roared demoniacal defiance in its claim for the square-rigged vessel. Christopher battled for his and the *Mayflower's* life. Such was the fury of the storm that he was driven three hundred miles off course and compelled to jettison a part of his cargo. But captain and ship made port together. Ever after they would work as one.

At home, Christopher found a baby daughter awaiting him. A small image of her mother, Christopher insisted that she be named Josian. Proudly, he carried her to All Saints Church for the christening. But like another baby who once came to live in the house beside the Stour, this one stayed scarce two years.

"What troubles you, Christopher?" Josian asked when he had lingered in port much longer than usual.

"Think not your question strange when a man has lost his only daughter?" Christopher felt Josian's eyes studying him as he whittled oak pegs for emergency ship repairs. He did not look up.

"Something troubles you besides the sadness. Your eyes tell me although your lips refuse."

Christopher arranged the pegs in a neat row, slipped his knife into its scabbard, and met Josian's gaze. "The shipping has moved from Harwich harbor," he said, "for that matter from most other coastal ports; it has concentrated in the Thames River out of London."

"A captain of a merchant vessel must follow the shipping; mayhap, we should move to the Thames," suggested Josian.

"But your kinfolk live here, and I am gone more than I am home."

"The Thames is not too far away," said Josian, "and need I mention that both my husband and my father have stout ships that can cover the distance?"

Christopher loaded the *Mayflower* with their household goods; he, Josian, and four-year-old Thomas sailed south along the shore of Essex County into the broad mouth of the Thames, and around its many curves upriver towards London. Christopher found a berth for his ship at Ratcliffe Mill, and a house for the family at Redriffe (Rotherhithe). The country was emerald green but so flat the river dikes had to be constantly watched. He and Josian both missed the cliffs of Harwich, but there were parks with flowers; and across the river from them, more than a hundred church spires, together with the Tower of London, pierced the sky. To the west was London Bridge. At the south end of the bridge, Christopher pointed out Southwark where they might attend plays given by a man named William Shakespeare at the well-known Globe Theater. Scarcely were they moved into the house, until it became a home by the birth of a son whom they named Roger after Christopher's brother.

No idle days now for the *Mayflower* and her captain. The wine trade kept them busy. Port entries show numerous trips to Rochelle, some few to Bordeaux and Gascony. There were times when Christopher felt the need of the harsh discipline of the North Sea to keep him in sailing trim, so occasionally he sought cargoes going north. Then, the *Mayflower* might be loaded with bolts of taffeta, stockings and perpetuanas, hops and salt; and on the return a hold full of fish. After the fish, several wine trips were necessary before his ship was again a "sweet ship."

Christopher's trade grew, his savings grew, his family grew. In 1613 baby Christopher was born but did not live, in 1615 daughter Joane and in 1618 Grace—two boys and two girls to watch for their father's sails and welcome him home. Christopher brought them tales from afar, of grape harvest in France, of "blows" in Biscay, of his latest bout with the North Sea. But the most fearful tale was one that happened right in the River Thames while the *Mayflower* lay at dock, something he had never dreamed happening to him. His crew had mutinied!

A man, pretending to be an inspector, had boarded the *Mayflower* to investigate, so he said, the drowning of a sailor, Edward Baillie, on the last trip out. Christopher had extended the usual courtesy of free run of the ship to question the crew, while he completed his charts in the captain's cabin.

Some time later he became aware of a commotion outside. Going out on deck, he faced a brawling drunken mob, his own crew armed with clubs, axes and knives. In the background was the inspector egging them on. Christopher realized in a flash what had happened. The inspector had been after trouble, not reports. He had stirred up the forecastle hands to raid the wine cargo, gotten them drunk, and urged a mutiny.

"Didst they—didst they kill you, Father?" asked round-eyed Joane who sat on her father's knee. Everyone laughed because of the obvious answer.

"How *did* you get out of it?" Thomas demanded.

Christopher held up his two fists for answer. "Seamen have sometimes called your father iron-fisted Jones. Not bad weapons on occasion. Anyway the sobered men are now repenting behind bars." Christopher shook his head. "Some of those men have been on my roster since the days of the *Marie Fortune*. Too much drinking makes fools of men. Take heed, boys."

Josian shuddered. "It could have turned out so differently. I think a merciful Providence gave a hand."

"And no doubt you are right," Christopher agreed.

6. On London Docks

TAVERNS and inns on the Thames swarmed with mariners. Ship captains from home ports and ports afar met at the Swan, the Angel, or the Boar's Head to pass the news of the day. Merchants came to discuss business over tankards of ale, to charter ships. There, the king's messenger read his Majesty's notices, edicts, items.

By the spring of 1619, ships bound for the New World received little more attention than those to the Continent. No longer did guns salute or banners wave as in the days of Sir Martin Frobisher, unless of course, royalty were on board. Each year two hundred fishing boats left Old England for the fisheries of New England and the Grand Banks of Newfoundland. Occasional ships sailed to Jamestown, Virginia, now an established colony.

In early spring, Londoners had witnessed a vessel depart for the James River with a unique cargo on board. One hundred orphans, six years and older, were herded across the ship's gangplank from dock to deck like so many sheep. The purpose was two-fold—to rid London of hungry mouths, and to furnish Jamestown colonists with help for weeding tobacco fields. When the children came of age, those that had survived the hazards of voyage, swamp fever, and Indian arrows would receive a plot of ground, a cabin, and cattle for their labor.

In March, Captain Thomas Dermer set sail for the Cape Cod region for the purpose of charting the New England coast. He took with him, to act as interpreter and guide, Tisquantum (Squanto) the Indian who had become a familiar figure on London docks. The circumstances under which Tisquantum came to England in the year 1614 made a story that stained the record of English sea captains. Now that he was gone, the tale was told and retold in taverns with the added hope that his returning to his native land might undo the mischief caused by the treachery at his leaving. For years captains had avoided a certain stretch of coast because of the revengeful hostility of its inhabitants.

Twenty Indian braves of Patuxet, including Tisquantum, had been lured aboard in New England waters by an English captain, Thomas Hunt, with the promise of trade. As soon as the red men were in the hold the hatches had been slammed shut and bolted. Sailing to Malaga, the wily Hunt had sold his human cargo as slaves to the Spaniards with a side profit to himself.

Tisquantum had somehow escaped slavery, finally reaching London where he worked for Merchant John

Slany of Cheapside, voyaging at one time as far as New-foundland. He learned to speak English but said little unless asked about his home country. Then he seemed to grow inches taller as he told of deer, wild turkeys, cod, and eel for the taking; and for the planting, Indian corn with kernels of red, blue, and yellow, wondrous good when roasted around campfires in the mighty forests of Patuxet.

How Patuxet would now appear to Tisquantum after having lived in London was a lively question discussed around inn tables. How would his civilized ways be regarded by his tribe?

Spring days were still damp and cold when tavern talk shifted to King James's hunt for the man he listed as personal and State Church enemy number one. Christopher was in port, relaxing over a mug of beer at the Boar's Head after unloading a cargo of French wine, when bagpipes and drum announced the king's messenger.

The velveted envoy mounted a raised platform and read from a parchment. The long formal preamble passed over Christopher as did far distant thunder warning of a squall that did not concern him; he but half listened, enjoying the mellowness of his drink.

". . . the most loved and dread Sovereign, King James I of England, and James VI of Scotland . . . to his most loyal subjects . . ." There followed a statement of the king's health, and a reminder of how the kingdom prospered under his reign. The concern of the communique proved to be an urgent alert to sea captains, inn-keepers, and merchants to be on the watch for a printer, William

Brewster. His crime? The said Brewster had printed (not written) a book, *Perth Assembly,* protesting five articles of the State Church creed, and by so doing insulted his Majesty, King James, head of the church.

The books had been printed on Brewster's privately-owned press in Choir Alley of Leyden, Holland. They had been distributed in Scotland and England by means of sealed wine casks.

Christopher wondered if he had unwittingly delivered any of the books. "Brewster . . . William Brewster," he had heard the name somewhere but couldn't quite reach it in his memory. "Brewster?" Where had he heard of the man?

And then he knew. William Brewster was one of the group of Separatists the Dutch captain had picked up in the face of a mob on the deserted coast north of Harwich. "Former postmaster of Scrooby, Cambridge man who had once been in the employ of the queen," so the Dutch captain said.

Christopher brought his attention back to the messenger's report. The libelous press had been confiscated, but the printer was at large, having evaded every effort of capture, though King James had combed both sides of the North Sea and the English Channel.

Instinctively, Christopher glanced through the square of window towards the Bloody Tower, a memorial of punishment to the enemies of royalty through the years. There, the hangman's noose, or the headman's block—it was said the stained ash block showed many deep gashes—or worse still, a living death in a cell where no warmth penetrated, awaited William Brewster if caught. Christopher couldn't but wish the printer luck.

The messenger read on ... "all possessors of ye seditious books, are commanded by his Majesty, under penalty of death if disobeyed, to bring said books to Cheapside, there to be publicly burned as a fitting end to perpetrators of heresy."

Drum and pipes sounded in the distance as the king's messenger went his way to other taverns. Christopher drained his mug. He pushed the king's message to the back of his mind, having shipping business to attend to. Besides, he had none of the books, and there wasn't a chance in seven seas he'd ever meet up with Printer Brewster.

And then it was a foggy June morning—1620. Low clouds hung over the Thames shutting in the soft coal smoke of chimneys ashore until it was hard to tell which was smoke, which was cloud. The *Mayflower's* masts at Ratcliffe Mill, as well as a score of other ships' masts, penetrated the low ceiling and were lost to sight.

Taking advantage of a low tide, Christopher climbed down a rope ladder to investigate his ship's hull. What he saw, put him in mood with the day. Her hull wore a plaster of barnacles and seaweed.

He was barely up on dock, when three men took shape out of the grime—a thick-set man, a tall thin man, and a man of average height and size. They came closer and peered intently at the *Mayflower's* name. Evidently satisfied, they turned toward Christopher.

"Captain Christopher Jones?" asked the thick-set man.

"None other," Christopher answered, and knew he sounded as he felt.

The man who had spoken introduced himself as Thomas Weston, ironmonger of London, and president of the Merchant Adventurers; his companions—indicating first the tall thin man—Robert Cushman, former woolcomber of Canterbury, now of Leyden, Holland; and John Carver, London merchant, but at present also of Leyden. They had come, Mr. Weston said, to talk over a business proposition with the captain.

Christopher's eye, practiced in appraising men, took in more than mere names and occupations as the man spoke. It told him that Thomas Weston could drive a sharp bargain, that spare, nervous Robert Cushman would be the over-conscientious type, that John Carver, a man about his own age, could be relied upon. Civility, after all he was in business, required that he invite the men aboard ship and listen to their proposition.

Seated in the great cabin, Thomas Weston came bluntly to the purpose of their visit. The committee's business, he said, was to find a ship of the proper size, whose captain would be interested in transporting a hundred or more planters to America for the purpose of establishing a colony in "ye North Virginia, twixt ye Delaware and Hudson rivers." He hastened to add, perhaps noting the startled impact his words had made on his listener, "Ye Merchant Adventurers will finance ye undertaking."

For a moment Christopher saw beyond the men in front of him, beyond the river's sooty fog, beyond the city of London. He was a boy standing on Harwich cliff. The sun shone down on ships sailing out of Harwich harbor, fifteen of them with a colony for the New World on board. Captains on poop decks, trumpets, guns...

Christopher's eyes met Thomas Weston's. He nodded. "Say on."

The planters, Mr. Weston explained, would be selected mainly from London and Leyden English craftsmen—tailors, merchants, weavers, woolcombers, printers; many of the men had formerly been farmers with a leaning toward that occupation. And many of them were of the Separatist persuasion, seeking religious freedom and not quick wealth—a stabilizing goal for a colony. There would be wives and children. After seven years of communal work, during which time the planters were to have two days a week to work for themselves, the property would be divided equally among the Adventurers and the planters, the planters keeping their houses and...

"Consort ships?" Christopher interrupted, interested in ship not land contracts.

"One, the *Speedwell,* a pinnace of sixty-ton-burden," said Weston. "The *Speedwell* will remain a year with the colony, but the convoy ship will return immediately, that is as soon as it can be loaded with lumber, sassafras, and furs." Mr. Weston stroked his beard. "Is the captain interested in the proposition, and would he show the committee through his ship?"

Always pleased to show the *Mayflower,* Christopher led the men on a tour of the ship, reeling off figures as to tonnage, sailing power, speed—at each quoted figure his spirits rising. He could see that Messrs. Weston, Cushman, and Carver were impressed. As to whether the ship were available, if the committee would return the following Monday, he would give the answer.

Christopher stood at the ship's rail watching the men disappear into the fog, and chided himself. Why had he not said *No?* Of course he wouldn't be going. He was too old for adventure—or was he? John Carver must be as old as he. Leaving age out of the question, there was the ship to be considered. He dare not risk the *Mayflower* on an unknown ocean; after all he was but fourth owner.

He could ask his partners' pleasure, the inner voice prompted. Christopher fell to wondering how an Atlantic crossing would compare with a North Sea voyage, the westerlies with nor'easters, New England with Old England . . .

Someone else would have to find out. He knew ruddy well he wouldn't. He was head of a family of five, his oldest thirteen, and the youngest, born last March, not yet three months. Christopher looked toward his home in Rotherhithe, but the fog held up a curtain. They had named the baby Jolin after big Jon (Jolin) of the *Swallow*. "Skipper Jon," Christopher dubbed him. Five children and he already fifty. No, adventure wasn't for him.

The voice persisted. Weren't heads of families . . .

Christopher turned from the rail. No more of this seesawing. His answer was *No*. He wouldn't even tell Josian of the committee's proposal.

But Josian found out—Josian always found out where Christopher was concerned—and, knowing that from a boy he had wanted to sail a colony to America, she encouraged him to go. She and the children would stay in Harwich, perhaps open the house on the Stour. The

ocean breeze would be bracing, the air cleaner than London air. "You would be back come Saint Martin's Day (November 11), wouldn't you?"

Christopher thought so; if not then by Christmas at the latest.

So, when the committee returned the following Monday, Captain Christopher Jones put his signature to an agreement with the Merchant Adventurers and the planters. What the agreement was, there is no record.

Christopher took his family to Harwich and helped them get settled. They were on the wharf to see him off, even Skipper Jon in his mother's arms. "Saint Martin's Day," shouted the boys as the *Mayflower's* men hove home her anchor. The family waved, and he waved until the ship sailed out of sight around the bend of the harbor.

With the *Mayflower* again anchored in the Thames, there was activity a-plenty. It was the Adventurers' business to build partitions in the 'tween deck and great cabin for the accommodation of passengers, Christopher's to careen the ship and muster a crew. Since he would be sailing a route unfamiliar to him, he must have mates who had been "across." He would need an expert cooper, whose job it was to see that the water, beer, and beef casks sprung no leaks, a ship's carpenter, doctor, gunners, quartermasters, boatswains—a crew totalling around twenty-five. He could muster the seamen from his regular roster; and from London docks, men and boys to climb ratlines and jostle cargo, but where to find mates?

Good fortune was leading, he felt, when at the Swan he met John Clark, a pilot who had sailed as mate on two voyages to Virginia; in fact, he had just returned from taking a load of kine from Ireland to the Jamestown colony, and was seeking a new berth. Mate Clark signed on. Robert Coppin of Harwich had voyaged to Cape Cod. Although that country was north of the *Mayflower's* destination, still, he had sailed the Atlantic. Coppin signed on as second mate. Young Doctor Giles Heale, licensed for a year by the Company of Barber Surgeons, signed with the intention of staying in America to practice medicine. A tall blond giant of a lad, John Alden, was pleased to go as cooper; he would join ship at Southampton.

By the middle of July barges began to arrive with the London and Essex planters and goods—Stephen Hopkins, the only passenger who had been in the New World before, with wife Elizabeth, three children, and two indentured servants. Christopher couldn't help noticing that Mistress Hopkins was large with child; the *Mayflower* might be honored with a birthing *en voyage*. From Dorking came the well-to-do shoe merchant, William Mullins with Mistress Mullins, son Joseph, and daughter Priscilla. At least the planters wouldn't lack for boots what with the cartons of them Merchant Mullins brought aboard.

And then there were the Billingtons. Why had Mr. Weston included such an un-church-like family with the religious group? Money, Christopher decided, was the answer when he saw they were to have the best cabin. He made a mental note that the Billington boys, Francis and John, would bear watching. Doctor Heale, and Robert Cushman, more nervous than ever, also embarked.

Since the doctor was planning to remain in America, he, too, wished to take considerable supplies, the best remedies of the day—butter which had been exposed fourteen days to the sun's rays to be used for aches and pains of joints caused by winter's cold, "instruments for bleeding, physic for purging, mandrakes and tobacco to be given as narcotics when necessary to cut, saw, or burn a limb." There were jars of simples and herbs; a roll of red cloth and a few discarded red petticoats to fasten over windows in case of a smallpox epidemic. "Red cloth," the doctor explained, "filters sun rays and helps to prevent scarring."

The London passengers were finally aboard. Not the least in Christopher's sight were the seven orphans that Mr. Weston gave into his charge. Later, they would be "put to" families from Leyden. Londoners paid three dollars passage money, collected by Mr. Weston, for each waif.

The *Mayflower* got underway. Forecastle hands manned the windlass and weighed anchor to the rhythm of a lusty sea chantey. Mate Clark stood on the quarterdeck, Captain Jones at his elbow, barking commands, younkers climbed rigging, unfurling canvas. The good ship sailed quietly around the familiar curves of the Thames, scattering the river's hundreds of swans, and leaving a foam-crested wake behind. Through the English Channel, past the chalk cliffs of Dover, the *Mayflower* made her way towards Southampton, the arranged rendezvous with her consort ship, the *Speedwell,* from Holland. As far as Captain Christopher Jones was concerned the voyage to America had begun.

At Southampton, Christopher tied up at West Quay. John Carver, and a Christopher Martin, appointed treasurer of supplies by the Adventurers, awaited the ship with a mountainous pile of provisions. To provision a ship it was necessary for men to go into the country and buy up wheat and live animals. The wheat was taken to a miller to be ground into flour, and the flour to a baker who baked it into tough, dry sea biscuits that would keep indefinitely. The animals were driven to a butcher who knew how to salt the meat down into the familiar "salt horse."

Christopher and mates Clark and Coppin were kept busy bossing the stowing of supplies into the ship's hold. Barrel after barrel of meat, beer, water, and wine was rolled across gangplank from dock to deck; boxes of cheese and biscuits; bags of turnips and onions, peas and prunes; firkins of butter, and perhaps the most important of all, lemons to prevent the dread scurvy. The *Mayflower's* crew were in good spirits at the sight of so much food and drink.

Wiry, red-headed Captain Standish, the appointed military leader of the colony, arrived with musket, cutlass, and trusty snaphance. A shallop with rudder and sail, for coastal navigation was stored, knocked-down, between decks.

At last the *Mayflower* was loaded. All eyes turned toward the harbor entrance. The *Speedwell* was overdue.

7. *"Quirimonies" and Various Delays*

SEVEN days went by, seven trying days for *Mayflower* captain and crew. More than once Christopher was reminded of the old executor's words, "Idle hands are a predilection of Satan." He stood at the taffrail, beneath which was the newly painted sign, *Mayflower of London*, and anxiously scanned the many ships entering the harbor for the consort ship, *Speedwell*.

At last she came, pennants waving jauntily! A welcome sight! Christopher measured her with professional eye. Something out of proportion there. Were her masts over-tall for her hull?

The *Speedwell* tied up alongside the *Mayflower*, a sixty-ton ship beside one of a hundred and eighty tons. At that, she was larger than the *Goodspeed* (40 tons) and the *Discovery* (20 tons) which had carried colonists to the Jamestown settlement. Captain Jones invited Captain Reynolds to his cabin to discuss the voyage. The *Speedwell* captain was worried. His ship would need some adjustments before continuing on. "She lists badly at times," he said. "Gave us several wettings coming down Channel."

Leydeners met Londoners on the dock; a few were old friends, the others strangers. Forecastle hands yarned overside with the newcomer crew. Just when friendly greetings turned into hot words, Christopher didn't know, but after Captain Reynolds left, he heard snatches of conversation as he paced the deck, fretting that operations were still in the word stage.

The trouble seemed to center around the agents, Treasurer Martin and Deacon Robert Cushman, John Carver saying little. "For what had all the money been spent?" the Leydeners wanted to know. It was they with whom the Adventurers had drawn up the contract and delivered the money.

Deacon Cushman pointed an accusing finger at Treasurer Martin. "Upon what I know not. Mr. Martin saith he neither can nor will give an account of it."

Christopher moved on. This was none of his business nor for his ears. Evidently the planters were short of money to clear harbor.

The next he overheard, Robert Cushman was being taken to task. It appeared that he had agreed to the dropping of a couple of clauses in the contract without consulting the body of planters—the one clause giving the planters two days a week to work for themselves, the other giving them their homes in the final settlement.

Now it was Treasurer Martin who wagged his finger at Deacon Cushman. " 'Tis an agreement fit only for thieves and bondslaves." He called the Adventurers "bloudsuckers."

Deacon Cushman defended himself on the lateness of time—Christopher agreed on that score—and that the Adventurers were losing interest. "Do they urge us or egg us?" he asked. "If we will not go, they are content to keep their money."

Someone suggested that perhaps Mr. Weston would come down from London to see them off and bring the sorely needed funds. After all it was he who had appointed the lavish Martin as treasurer. In the meantime there were passenger adjustments to be made. Ninety would sail in the *Mayflower,* thirty in the *Speedwell.*

Mr. Weston came down from London bringing the new contract to be signed. When the Leydeners refused, he left in a temper, telling them, "From now on you will stand on your own legs."

Now what? Time was going by. The *Mayflower* was ready to sail. The *Speedwell* was ready, but no funds to clear harbor. More bickering.

Christopher saw his sailors getting a wrong impression of "ye saints" as the church people termed themselves, calling them "psalm-singing landlubbers what quarreled and fit like ye fighting cocks." And in turn the saints lifted questioning eyebrows at the forecastle hands' games at dice, and cards, their shocking language, their worldly songs. Feelings between passengers and crew were becoming strained.

A letter was delivered to the *Mayflower* which Christopher turned over to John Carver. It proved to be a letter from the Leydeners' pastor, John Robinson, in which he advised "much wisdome and charitie" in their dealings. "Store up therefore patience," he admonished.

Patience, patience—Christopher felt his supply of that commodity running low as he paced the deck.

The letter did its work. "Quirimonies and complaints" subsided. The planters decided to sell some of their butter to procure funds for harbor clearance.

Seamen lugged sixty firkins (forty pounds to the firkin) from the *Mayflower* hold—muttering. No chanteys, now. Christopher was thankful there were no desertions.

It was the fifth of August, and the ships were about to weigh anchor. Christopher was standing on the dock exchanging last minute words with Captain Reynolds, when he noticed some of the *Speedwell* passengers hurrying a last arrival on board. Somebody's grandmother, he surmised, the way the figure was swathed. Poor judgment to take one so elderly on so hazardous a voyage. As the group passed by he noticed the newcomer's fine hand-turned shoe buckles. So—the person was a grandfather, not a grandmother. Most as direful!

Southwestward the two ships put to sea, the *Speedwell* following in the wake of the *Mayflower*. They were outside Lyme Bay with a hundred miles behind them, when Mate Clark called Christopher's attention to the lowered pennant of the consort ship, a signal that the captain wanted a conference.

Captain Reynolds reported that the *Speedwell* was leaking badly, that he "durst not put further to sea until she was mended." Captains and mates conferred. It was

decided to tack ship and steer for the nearest port—
Dartmouth.

At Dartmouth, carpenters and seamen from both ships
spent four days going over the leaky *Speedwell*. Deacon
Cushman hovered near. He was supercargo on the *Speedwell*, a sort of governor over passengers to oversee the
apportioning of provisions and supplies. "She is as leakie
as a sieve," he declared. "If ever we make a plantation,
God works a miracle."

While at Dartmouth, Christopher had to put Treasurer
Martin who was supercargo on the *Mayflower* in his
place. Sailors angrily complained of his "ignorante bould-
ness," that he tried to boss them in things he knew nothing about. If only the captain would permit them to treat
the man to an old time keel-hauling (pulling an offender
by rope under the keel of a ship from starboard to larboard), it might trim his importance down to size. But
Christopher, who had handled a mutiny singlehanded,
was equal to Treasurer Martin.

August 23—Once more the *Mayflower* and *Speedwell*
put to sea. Southwest by west, past Land's End and the
Scilly Islands. Three hundred miles of ocean behind them,
and again the *Speedwell* signaled for a conference. The
ships hove to.

Captain Reynolds complained that his ship was "so
leakie as he must bear up or sinke at sea, for they could
scarce free her with much pumping."

Deacon Cushman again added his doleful bit. "Poore
William King and I do strive who shall be meate first for
ye fishes."

Nothing to do but turn back. The *Mayflower* shortened sail to match the *Speedwell's* limping gait. Together the ships crept into Plymouth Sound and tied up at Barbican Quay. There, expert advice could be had from the shipyard that built Queen Elizabeth's navy. And there, the *Speedwell* was condemned as unseaworthy. She was over-masted, causing her seams to work open when she was pressed with sail.

Now that no consort ship was going, the contract to transport colonists to America "in company with a consort," was void. The planters anxiously inquired, "Would Captain Jones consider the voyage without consort? If so, could he take a few more passengers on the *Mayflower,* say twelve?"

A sleepless night of tormenting thought, a night in which Christopher paced the poop deck, or leaned on the ship's rail vainly searching for an answer in the star-mirrored black water of the harbor. It had been seven weeks since he, in high spirits, had weighed anchor in the Thames at Rotherhithe, time enough with the existing fair wind to have anchored in the New World. But here he was, tied up at Plymouth, England, instead.

What did it all mean? Was he not supposed to cross the Atlantic? How should he answer the planters' query? Never had a colonist ship gone alone. Always, there had been two or more consort ships. With no second ship he would be obliged to remain with the planters until they could construct some type of shelter. The westerlies ... an unknown ocean ... an unknown anchorage at journey's end. His better judgment told him a September crossing was too late.

He thought of John Carver and the planters awaiting

his answer. They were dependent on him. Many of them had invested their all. But dare he take the risk? What about his own family?

Dawn lightened the eastern sky. A land breeze began its work of sweeping the harbor of night mists, making way for the tardy September sun. Over there, from where the light came, Skipper Jon would be up. Jon always beat the sun. Soon the family would be gathered around the breakfast table. Josian would have set his place at the head. They would bow their heads over the trenchers, ask a blessing on the porridge, and an added special blessing for him. They had faith in him. These others had faith in him, too. His courage rose with the sun to meet their confidence.

Christopher saw the drawn-faced planters—there had been no sleep for them either—relax when he told them he would go. But twelve passengers more was the *May-flower's* limit. They must decide who was to go, who to remain.

Christopher set his seamen to work shifting baggage. He would leave mates Clark and Coppin in charge while he went ashore to study the splendid maps to be found at Plymouth, and read the reports of captains who had been across. He would locate a ship going Harwich way and send word to Josian concerning the change in sailing date. Perhaps he best not mention the lack of consort— only various delays.

As he dressed in shore hosen and boots, velvet jerkin and plumed hat, a most welcome sound came to him— a parody on an old sea chantey:

To Plymouth! To Plymouth! It is a gallant town.
And there we will have a quart of wine with nutmeg brown,
Diddle down!
The Gallant Ship, the Mermaid, the Lion, hanging stout,
Did make us to spend our sixteen pence all out.
Diddle down!

His forecastle hands were singing as they shunted baggage about. So long as they sang—no matter the song, no matter the frown of passengers—the forecastle morale of his ship was healthy. But when men muttered . . .

Christopher returned to the *Mayflower* mid weeping farewells of those who were sailing and those remaining behind. He was sorry to learn Deacon Cushman would not be going. He would gladly have exchanged waspish supercargo Martin for the nerve-wracked Cushman. He felt the man was more sinned against than sinning. The deacon would be coming the next ship over. In the meantime, he would try to straighten out the contract between Adventurers and planters.

Christopher boarded ship behind a young couple, the man having fairly to carry his weeping wife across the gangplank. She stretched out her arms as if to someone left behind. He later learned the couple were William and Dorothy Bradford. They had left their five-year-old son in Leyden with Pastor Robinson.

What? Surely the be-muffled grandfather wouldn't be going! But there he was, coming across the gangplank. With space at a premium, why was the old one considered so important? There was scarcely more than standing room in the cabins 'tween deck. He was pleased when

John and Catherine Carver with their six indentured young folk came aboard. Carver was a man that gave one a feeling of confidence just to have him along.

At four o'clock when the tide was right, the morning of September 6, Christopher took his place on the poop and gave the commands of departure, mates Clark and Coppin relaying them to helmsman and up fo'ard. Before a "fine small gale" the *Mayflower,* riding deep in the water because of her heavy burden but with a bone of foam curling back from her bow, retraced her entry into Plymouth Sound more than a week before. As always, Christopher thrilled at the sight of his ship taking over her work. The spritsail pulled like a small stallion up forward. Main and foresails bellied their sheets taut. The lateen mizzen pushed as if making up for lost time. "A ruddy ship, a ruddy fine ship!" he said aloud.

Whimsically, Christopher thought back to the day of Sir Martin Frobisher's departure from Harwich harbor to plant a colony in the New World. Except for captain's apparel, the splendid ship, and the gulls doing their screeching best—there, the comparison ended. No consort ships, no gun salute, no golden chain, no royal farewell for the *Mayflower* and captain. Royalty was not interested in her humble passengers. Christopher bore the highest social rank on board. England, in 1620, recognized four classes—gentlemen (dukes, earls, etc.), citizens, yeomen, and the laboring class. Christopher was of citizen class, his passengers, yeomen and laborers. No, King James would not be interested in any *one* of his hundred and two passengers.

Christopher turned to his cabin for a change of clothes,

the hosen and footwear for heavy high top boots, the velvet jerkin for waterproof leather jacket, the plumed hat for wool cap that Josian had lined with down and quilted. He placed the shore clothes in his sea chest, wondering when he would wear them again. Not for debarking on the wild savage shore of North Virginia, of that he was sure.

8. Westward Sailed the Mayflower

IT was the morning of September eleven, and the fifth out of Plymouth. The "fine small gale" from the east held. The Atlantic appeared as a great molten silver disc with the dome of sky meeting its rim. In the center of this immense nowhere sailed the lone *Mayflower*. Log and line checked against hour glass revealed she was averaging four knots.

Words of a psalm floated up to Captain Christopher Jones on the quarter-deck as he peered into the ship's binnacle-enclosed compass.

> *They that go down to the sea in ships*
> *their business to do,*
> *In waters great the Lord's work see,*
> *in the deep his wonders, too.*

His passengers began the day with prayers on deck when weather permitted. This morning he was aware of more adult voices joining the children's quavery soprano than before. Must be the older folk were getting their sea legs against the ocean's swells. Children always recovered first.

The prayer that followed was longer than usual and by a voice he didn't remember having heard before, a voice with literary Cambridge accent. Curious, he stepped to the rail and looked down. The man *was* a stranger. Had he picked up a stowaway at Plymouth? And then he noticed the hand-turned shoe buckles. Why, the man was none other than the beswathed "grandfather." But this man wasn't really old, about his own age or a little younger. He appeared virile, energetic. Must have been ailing to have been so bundled when he boarded ship.

About to turn from the rail, Christopher noticed one of the orphans hallooing the man from a swirl of deck cordage. The youngster made a megaphone with his hands. "E-l-d-e-r B-r-e-w-s-t-er," he called.

The name gave Christopher a start. His mind raced. Bits of memory fell into place as parts of a puzzle— Cambridge student, Scrooby postmaster, flight into Holland by way of Dutch ship, the king's search for the printer, the grandfather guise. So, he had the notorious Brewster on board! He chuckled remembering he had said when leaving Plymouth, "King James wouldn't be interested in any *one* of his hundred and two passengers." Wouldn't he now? If his Majesty had known, there would have been more ado—of a different kind of course—than attended the sailing of Sir Martin Frobisher.

The children clustered about the elder. Francis Billington climbed a forbidden ratline to attract his attention. Those boys, the six- and nine-year-olds holding onto his hands, the boys with the odd names, Wrestling and Love, must be his sons. The man had to be a good sort, Christopher told himself, if children took to him. He chuckled again. You've found the perfect hideout from King James's wrath, Mr. Brewster—a ship. And this ruddy ship will take you to the refuge of the New World.

Fair weather persisted except for occasional wind or rain squall; so did seasickness for some of the passengers. They crawled up the hatchways and lay on deck hoping the salt air would relieve their nauseous misery. Now, it was the sailors who lifted not eyebrows, but voices in sneering taunts and jeering quips. The sprawling landlubbers were in their way.

One "proud and lustie" seaman had less tolerance than his fellows. He "did not let to tell them that he hoped to cast halfe of them over-board before they came to their journey's end." When feebly remonstrated for his words he "would curse and swear most bitterly."

The *Mayflower* carried a rule against cursing or abusing passengers, also irons and ferula for any guilty of such. But before punishment could catch up with him, this "proud and very profane yonge man" was taken suddenly ill with a "grievous disease." In a delirium terrible to hear, he died the same day.

Death on the *Mayflower!* Now Captain Jones must act the role of chaplain. A plank for a bier was brought from the hold. The body was sewn into a canvas shroud, weighted head and foot, and laid on the plank.

Passengers gathered on deck in a silent group. Seamen stood with bared heads. The sea droned monotonously; the wind moaned a dirge in the rigging; blocks creaked a weird off-beat rhythm, as Christopher read a passage from the ship's dog-eared prayer book. Sailors lifted the bier to the ship's rail, and slid the body into the ocean. There was one loud "ploump" and all was over.

The harassed passengers saw the incident as a judgment of God upon the haughty youth. The superstitious forecastle hands were not sure that it wasn't. Afterward, disdain was shown in looks only, not words.

They were half-sea over, and it was October. Captain Jones with mates Clark and Coppin watched the western horizon. How much longer could the elements hold the straining westerlies in leash? Warning signs had already appeared—a head sea of ominous swells, threatening clouds at sunset, a school of porpoises hurrying by without stopping to investigate the queer wooden fish.

The wind backed around to the west and met the ship head on. Since no ship can sail into the eye of the wind, the *Mayflower* now had to beat her way to windward by sailing a zig-zag course, first on one tack, then the other, and "All hands" to put the ship about each time.

The rising westerly quickly whipped ocean swells into graybacks that challenged the ship for trespassing the closed-season seaway. Christopher tensed as he took his stance on the poop against the ever-strengthening gale. He and the *Mayflower* had ridden out many a nor'easter. But for the human cargo he carried, he could almost feel elation over the coming battle. He gave passengers strict orders to stay below.

The ship hurdled wave after wave. To begin the hurdle she lifted her bow and climbed, sometimes leaped up to meet the sea. At the crest she paused, then plunged with a rolling dive into the green trough below, shipping swirling water over the lee side onto her low main deck.

Christopher knew the 'tween deck passengers, unless tied to bunks, were being tossed about like driftwood on an open sea, that the air down there with gunports and hatches closed must be foul. But compared to his soddenly-wet, sleep-starved, poorly clad crew, some of them hardly more than boys, taking the punishment of icy spindrift that bit into their flesh like a cat-o'-nine tails, the voyagers were reasonably well off in their protection from the storm.

To his horror, as the *Mayflower* began one of her climbs, Christopher saw the hatch cover lift, and a young man emerge. Before he could shout a warning, a sea crashed aboard, seized the fellow, and hurled him over the rail. "Man overboard!" he bellowed. Not a chance in a thousand!

"Man overboard!" the forecastle hands took up the cry.

Grabbing boathooks, sailors swarmed across the reeling deck holding to emergency lifelines. "He's caught a trailin' lanyard," someone yelled above the din.

Hauling on the line, they hooked the half-drowned victim as they would a marlin, and just in time. The young man was John Howland, one of John Carver's indentured servants. He was reported "something ill" after his experience.

Day and night the westerly raged. The sea rose up in maniacal fury. The whipstaff proved inadequate to keep the ship on course. "Steer with the yoke," Christopher ordered. This meant fastening two lines to the end of the tiller. Two sets of additional men would haul to larboard or to starboard as conned by the pilot.

As the men were changing steering methods, the wind turned the *Mayflower* to leeward. The waves struck her broadside.

"Hard to starboard!" Christopher roared down the speaking hatch. And then he felt more than heard something give way.

Captain, mates, carpenter, picked seamen hurried below. An awful stench met them—a wonder the candle burned—the stench of unwashed bodies, of seasickness, of the "bucket," the only sanitary convenience.

One of the ship's main beams had cracked and buckled. The sagging deck let down streams of water. The sea pounded against the *Mayflower's* hull as if to make short work of the wounded vessel. At any moment another beam might give way.

Crewmen set their shoulders against the beam but it would not budge. The situation appeared hopeless until a Leydener remembered a "great iron scrue" he had brought along. (Speculation suggests that the screw was a part of William Brewster's printing press.) With the help of the screw the beam was moved back into place and then reinforced with timbers.

Pale-faced, anxious-eyed voyagers turned to Christopher. Dare they go on, or should they turn back and run before the westerly?

Christopher rubbed his salt-stiffened brow. He spoke slowly. "The *Mayflower* is a ruddy good ship. She is tight below the waterline. If not over-pressed with sail I feel she can make it."

The captain's confidence became the voyagers' confidence. The decision was to go on.

The storm did not abate. Gale after gale attacked the weakened *Mayflower* with mast-high seas. Christopher met the height of the gale by lying "a-hull"—all sails furled, topmasts struck, and helm lashed down keeping the ship's head to the wind. The *Mayflower* seemed to appreciate the respite. She responded "like a duck with its head under its wing asleep on the turbulent sea." For days Christopher alternated between beating to windward and lying "a-hull."

October dragged by. The storm subsided. It was reported to Christopher that Mistress Hopkins' time had come. He thought of his own Skipper Jon. The cabins below were not fit for a birthing. "Bring Mistress Hopkins to the captain's cabin," he ordered, and moved his gear in with mates Clark and Coppin in the great cabin. Records have it that Captain Christopher Jones was the first to congratulate Stephen and Elizabeth Hopkins on the birth of their son, Oceanus.

Another burial at sea. Young William Butten of London had died. This time Elder Brewster read the service. A birth and a death left the passenger list the same count —one hundred and two.

November 8—Christopher's sixth sea sense told him the *Mayflower* was nearing land. He took a noon sight on

69

the sun. The ship was coming in on the forty-second parallel of latitude in a direct line for Cape Cod. She had drifted off course in the storm. Late afternoon showed the deep blue of ocean depth turning to the green of shoaler water. He took soundings, but the deep-sea lead spun to the end of its line and found no bottom.

The setting sun drew the wind away with it, leaving the *Mayflower's* sails limp. At midnight the dim last quarter of the moon came up out of the sea, its crescent pointing westward. Early morning brought a cat's-paw

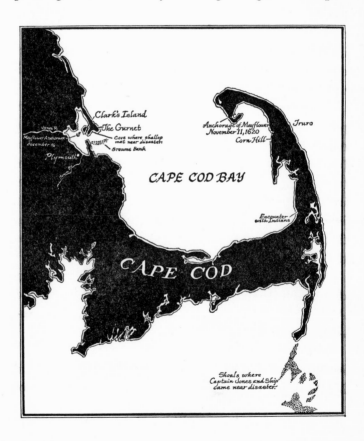

of breeze. The sails began to fill. Christopher proceeded cautiously, ears alerted to both lookout top and leadsman's chant. At six-thirty he was rewarded.

"L-a-n-d Ho!" shouted the lookout.

"Bottom at eighty fathoms!" sang the leadsman.

Passengers swarmed up from below crowding the ship's rail. They saw a long gray line to the west that did not move with the cloud procession. Closer in, Christopher recognized from having read, and Coppin from having been there before, the heights of Truro on the low-lying arm of Cape Cod.

Land, any land was gratifying to land-starved eyes. It caused "not a little rejoicing," wrote William Bradford in his report. But the land was not that designated in their patent. A conference was called. It was decided to head off and sail with the wind toward the south following the arm of the cape.

All went well until about noon when suddenly, without warning, the *Mayflower* glided onto a shelf of hidden sandy shoals. Foaming, racing tide rips began to tear at her. The wind died. How to get off? Christopher found himself in the most hazardous predicament he and ship had ever been in.

The terrified passengers fell to their knees, beseeching help from above. A south wind began to blow. Cautiously, slowly, Christopher edged the *Mayflower* off the shelf, then made for the safety of deep water. There, he hove to for the night.

The next morning a conference was called with the unanimous decision to retrace their way northward before the south wind back to the welcoming arm of Cape Cod.

Patent or no patent, anything was better than trying to find a way through the treacherous shoals.

About noon on November the eleventh, Saint Martin's Day—the day he was to have tied up at Harwich wharf —Christopher brought the *Mayflower* around the tip of Cape Cod and anchored in "ye fine harbor," of the New World.

So joyful were the voyagers to see the "goodly land . . . wooded to ye brink of ye sea," they fell upon their knees and "blessed ye God of heaven, who had brought them over ye vast and furious ocean and delivered them from all ye perils. . . ."

From the quarter-deck Christopher heard the prayer, and remembering the south wind at the shoals, did not disagree. But where did *he* fit in? After all, he had sailed the ship—first mate, perhaps, to that Higher Power.

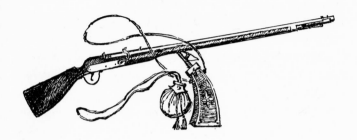

9. *A Place of Habitation*

LATE Friday afternoon, the seventeenth of November, Christopher climbed through a thicket of sassafras and beach plum to the top of a sandy hillock that he might have a better view of the surroundings. He studied the graying sky; did it threaten snow? His eye followed each curve and cove of the irregular shoreline, swept the adjacent forest of oak, pitch pine, and juniper—no sign of the exploring party.

On Wednesday, a group of sixteen men led by Captain Standish, had been permitted rather than encouraged to go on a two-day exploring expedition. Though the explorers were armed with cutlass and musket, and wore corselets of mail, and helmets, the undertaking without support of boat offshore appeared hazardous, even foolhardy, to some of the older men. What dangers the forest concealed no one knew—dangers from savage beasts, dangers from savage men. The group of sixteen had not been seen nor heard from, except for a signal fire on the ocean side of the cape. But could one be sure whose fire it was? The two days were up. The men were due back at the ship.

Governor Carver joined Christopher on the hillock. John Carver had been elected governor and a compact of government drawn up the first day of anchorage at Cape Cod. The smell of burning juniper and of melting tar wafted up to them from the beach below where men were repairing and assembling the shallop. Near the water's edge, a group of wives and children anxiously watched for husbands and fathers. They had come ashore earlier in the day, the women to wash clothes in a fresh water pond, the children to dig clams and have a turn on the beach. Out in the bay whales played an endless game of follow-the-leader, snuffing, sounding, spouting.

"Yon whale," said Christopher, "are more numerous than ye Greenland whale. Hadst we harping irons and trying equipment, we might try out 'twixt three to four thousand pounds of oil."

John Carver shook his head regretfully. " 'Twould pay our debt to ye Merchant Adventurers twice over."

The two fell silent as they scanned the shoreline. An expectant hush settled over all as the dim disc of sun lowered in the west. Builders laid aside their tools. Even the gulls soared without clamor.

A child's high-pitched voice broke the hush. "Canst see father?"

The mother's reply was inaudible to the men on the hillock. Christopher felt a snowflake brush his forehead, then another.

Again the child's insistent voice—"Canst see him n-o-w?"

As if in answer there came a volley of musket shot from the forest far down the shore. And then dark figures, small in the distance, began to come out of the woods onto the beach. No one spoke, hardly dared to breathe. Everyone was counting.

". . . thirteen, fourteen, fifteen . . . sixteen." They were all there! All sixteen men were coming back to the ship.

Children shouted and ran to meet their fathers. Women suddenly remembered much to talk about. Gulls screamed at the burst of noise.

Christopher sent the longboat to give the explorers a lift. He and John Carver walked along the beach with the families and friends to escort them in.

On board ship, the men emptied pockets and waist-coats of a kind of grain they had found buried in baskets under mounds of sand on a hillside. Besides the shelled grain, there were thirty-six full ears. The planters had never seen anything like it before.

Christopher immediately recognized the *find* as the corn Tisquantum had told about on the docks of London, "Indian corn with kernels of red, blue, and yellow, won-drous good . . ."

"Is the corn land suitable for habitation?" John Carver wanted to know.

The land, the men reported had a "spit's depth of excellent black earth atop the sand," but far from a sup-ply of sweet water which was mostly in ponds that might dry up in the summer.

Had they seen any Indians?

"Five or six with a dog on ye beach, but they fled into ye woods when we would speak with them."

"Game?"

"Ye greatest store of fowl that ever we saw—partridges, geese, ducks . . ."

"And deer," added another. "We judge them to be plentiful from ye many tracks about ye ponds."

The shallop assembled, Christopher urged the planters to make haste in finding a place of settlement. He must get his ship and crew back to England before provisions ran out. The bosun was all for unloading the planters and their goods on shore and letting them shift for themselves, but Christopher would have none of it. He volunteered to help in locating a place. In recognition of his kindness, the planters made him leader of thirty-four explorers that set out in shallop and longboat on a second discovery.

From the *Mayflower* Christopher had seen to the south what appeared to be two rivers flowing into the bay, separated by a narrow breadth of high land. Reminded of the excellent harbor the Stour and Orwell had carved out in Harwich, he thought these streams also, might provide good anchorage for ships. He steered for the river mouths but a sleety northeast wind churned up such a surf, he was obliged to lower sail and row for shore. "It blowed and did snow all that day and night, and froze withal." The next day the shallop reached the rivers which proved to be more of the nature of tide estuaries, and deep enough only for boats.

All day, in six inches of snow, Christopher and men

tramped up and down the land separating the rivers, the shallop following in the larger stream. They camped at night under a thick growth of pines, and were able to shoot three fat geese and six ducks for their supper, "which they did eat with soldiers' stomachs."

Finding no suitable place for habitation, the explorers turned back, crossed the smaller stream in an Indian dugout canoe which lay on the bank, and climbed the hill where the corn had been found on the previous discovery. With short sword they dug into the now snow-covered and frozen mounds, recovering ten bushels of corn, a bag of beans, and a jug of oil. Some of the men wished to explore farther, but Christopher read storm warnings in the black clouds gathering on the wintry horizon and was anxious for his ship. Promising to send the shallop back, he set sail for the *Mayflower* with the corn and the more weary of the men.

He found the ship had gained a passenger in his absence. A son had been born to Mistress Susanna White, and waited in a wicker cradle for his father to name him.

"The day you were born," said William White to his tiny son, "your father was wandering in a strange land in search of a home. Your name shall be Peregrine which means wanderer."

The immediate danger to the ship proved to be from aboard, not from the impending storm. In spite of the vigilance of Christopher and crew, the *Mayflower* came near disaster. Francis Billington, taking advantage of his father's absence, made squibs, and shot off a charged fowling piece in the family cabin. A half-barrel of gunpowder stood nearby, and powder that the boy had spilled lay on the floor. Reporting on the incident, William Bradford concludes, "by the grace of God no harm done." The report does not say what the bosun did to Francis. Whatever it was, he most likely did not wait until "whuppin' day" to do it.

Winter was upon them. One question was uppermost in everyone's mind, where was there a place of habitation?

Mate Coppin came forward with a suggestion. When he had been in these parts on a former voyage, the ship had anchored in a fine harbor with navigable river. He thought the place was on the other arm of the bay directly opposite to the *Mayflower's* anchorage. Maps in the captain's cabin by former explorers, Samuel de Champlain and John Smith, confirmed Coppin's report of a harbor. John Smith's map gave the name of the harbor as Plimouth.

Christopher looked across the expanse of water. Might ruddy well be eight leagues, he estimated.

A council was called and the decision made to send out a third discovery party to encompass the whole of Cape Cod bay. Governor Carver and Captain Standish would head the group of ten picked men including William Bradford. Christopher appointed mates Coppin and Clark to captain the shallop, chose able seamen to manage sail and oars, and a "lusty seaman" to steer. (The planters knew little about boats.)

Wednesday, December the sixth, a cold hard winter day, the shallop bravely stood forth about noon. Solemnly, those on board the *Mayflower* watched it depart, frail Catherine Carver, quiet Rose Standish, and young

Dorothy Bradford standing at the rail together. The departure was all the more solemn because one of the orphans had died that morning, the lad put to the Carvers; and James Chilton, family man, was sick unto death. But the shallop could not wait for death nor illness— the perils of winter faced the whole company.

The morning following the explorers' departure, Christopher went ashore with some of his crew for the purpose of hunting. Fresh food was needed, and besides, the ship's provisions must be hoarded for the home voyage. Returning in the evening, he found the *Mayflower* in deep mourning. Dorothy Bradford had fallen overboard and drowned. No one seemed to be able to tell just how the drowning happened. Christopher looked at the stout oak rail of his ship, at the cold but reasonably quiet harbor; he thought of the day in Plymouth, England, when the young woman had reluctantly boarded ship . . . and wondered.

The next day James Chilton died. After services by Elder Brewster, the body was taken ashore and buried in the sand of the Point beside the grave of the orphan lad. Meantime a gale blew in from the Atlantic. Anxiously, those on board ship watched the west for signs of the shallop.

"Shallop, ahoy," called the maintop lookout on Friday afternoon of the fifteenth. Everyone crowded the *Mayflower's* rail to watch the shallop come in. What a battered boat she was! With broken mast, makeshift sail, and crippled rudder, she limped in somehow on a straight course from across the bay. Halloos were exchanged between ship and boat, and then the breathless hush of intense searching for familiar faces. This time the hush continued, those on the *Mayflower* being acutely aware that one in the shallop would not find the face he sought at the rail. William Bradford climbed the ship's rope ladder, spoke briefly with Elder Brewster, and went below to his cabin.

The explorers brought back not only a good report—they had found a place of habitation, two in fact—but also tales of fierce encounter with Indians and with storm. Captain Standish displayed a bundle of eighteen arrows, tipped with deer-horn, eagle-claws, and brass, that had been shot at them the first morning out. The Indians had been frightened off by his trusty snaphance and his comrades' muskets. "They had fought Indians! And they were still alive!"

As the discovery party had sailed on, the gale from the Atlantic had whipped the bay into a fury, broken their rudder, split their mast into three pieces, cast their sail into the sea, and finally, had driven them into a cove of roaring breakers. Had it not been for the "lusty seaman" they were all agreed, they might now be at the bottom of the harbor. Pulling mightily with oars, since the tiller was useless, he had turned the shallop, shouting to those that rowed, "If ye be men, about with her else we are cast away," the which they did with speed.

In pitch darkness with driving rain and snow, they had come under the shelter of an island. There, Mate Clark with a few volunteers went ashore, and stumbling and groping amid black copses for wood, succeeded in building a fire. In gratefulness, the men had named the island for him—Clark's Island.

Christopher felt that his men had given a good account of themselves, and the planters were "much comforted" by the report of their ten. From having no abiding place, they now had the choice of two—the island, and another on the mainland where the men had found deserted corn fields on the banks of a "deep-running brook of sweet water" (Town Brook).

Had they sounded the harbor Christopher wanted to know.

Mates Coppin and Clark assured him they had, and a "goodly harbor" it was, much larger than Cape Cod, with the sea shut out by a beachhead of sand and rock and trees withal.

"But ye harbor is difficult of entrance," conceded Mate Clark. With a piece of charcoal he drew a rough map on the palm of his hand, indicating two high points of land (Gurnet and Saquish) at the harbor entrance with a cove between. "Ye cove where ye shallop all but met disaster," he explained. To the left of the cove he drew a sand bar (Browns Bank), around which a ship on entering the harbor would have to make an almost right-angled turn.

Christopher squinted at the drawing. "A ship would be hard-pressed to make the turn in a wind west by north."

Mate Clark agreed.

Two days later, the shallop, equipped with a new set of sails and repaired rudder, led the *Mayflower* the twenty-five miles across the bay. At the entrance to the harbor, a breeze sprung up from west by north and, as Christopher had predicted, the ship was unable to make the turn. She had to retrace her way to Cape Cod. Successful on a try the following day, the *Mayflower* came to anchor in twenty feet, a mile and a half from shore in Plymouth harbor.

And now came the ordeal of final decision of settlement. Again, the planters asked Christopher to head the group; three days, beginning each with prayer, they searched by boat . . . by foot . . . and debated. A third suitable location was found, making the decision still more difficult, a river three miles across the harbor from Clark's Island, not the great navigable river Coppin had told about, but a "very pleasant river" running through fertile land, salt meadows, and dense woods. The planters named the very pleasant river *Jones River* after the man who was piloting them about.

And still they debated. William Bradford and a few favored Clark's Island because of easy defense; but there was no running water. Others favored the river because of the fertility of the soil; but it was pointed out that the heavy growth of timber would prevent seeing a foe until the enemy was upon them. The majority were for the brook with its adjoining deserted corn fields. The land seemed to be waiting for them.

Christopher looked at the fields and wondered what story lay behind the fields' desertion. He judged by the growth of brush that whatever it was must have happened at least three, possibly four years before.

Another advantage of the brook location—they could land without wading. A large rock jutted out from the beach into water deep enough at high tide for the shallop to anchor beside it. The men went ashore and climbed the hill that rose steeply from the landing. The entire countryside, as well as the bay and ocean beyond, could be seen from the height. Captain Standish pointed out that the hill would be an excellent sight for their ordnance; neither man nor ship could approach without being seen. And so it was, that the location of the first townsite in New England was decided upon—deserted corn fields on the bank of a sweet water brook on the slope of a hill rising steeply from Plymouth harbor.

The colonists' immediate problem was solved, but not Christopher's. *When* would he be able to set sail for home? The planters wished to detain him at their investors' and their expense. Christopher, though his inner self protested sorely, felt he should stand by until the colony he had brought over had reasonable shelter, and its safety assured.

10. The Long Winter

IT WAS Christmas morning. Christopher stood at the poop deck rail and watched the shallop dim into the raw mist. The planters were going ashore to begin their place of habitation, "some to fell timbers, some to saw, some to rive, and some to carry." First, they would build a common house near the water's edge, then a platform on the hill for their ordnance. They would build homes along a single street (Leyden Street) leading steeply up the hill from the common house to the ordnance platform, and parallel to the north bank of the sweet water brook.

The men had gone ashore willingly, but somewhat depressed. Not depressed because they were working on Christmas; they did not believe in celebrating Christmas, a holiday of pagan origin. They were depressed because beginning this day those on shore were "reduced to drinking water." They believed (as did everyone in 1620) that beer was necessary to health. The planters' own store of beer had been used up, and Christopher was forced to ration the ship's supply that there might be enough for the return voyage. Beer was specified in the ship's articles the crew had signed; besides, water stored in casks became foul and unfit to drink on a lengthy voyage.

Christmas in New England! How different from Christmas in Old England! Christopher's thoughts spanned the ocean. In Harwich, church bells would be ringing, mummers performing in the streets, houses decked with ivy, bay, and laurel. His pulse quickened as he thought of pulling the door latch of the stone house on the Stour, surprising his family at dinner. His place would be set and waiting for him, he knew. On the table would be a roast goose, browned to a turn in the way only Josian knew, and a suet pudding full of fruit. But he was here, and they . . . he sighed, hoping they were not worrying too much about him.

Christopher blew on his frost-bitten hands to warm them while thoughts of home warmed his heart. After dinner the family would play hot cockles, shoe-the-mare, sing carols; nor would Skipper Jon be left out of the fun. Many a willing foot would take him for a "Ride a cock horse to Banbury cross." The house would fill with guests. On Christmas there was no master and servant segregation, no burgess and commoner—all classes gathered at the great house to feast, drink, and make merry together.

Great house! Hm-m-m! Wasn't the *Mayflower* the "great house" in New England? Shouldn't he hold open house on deck? Didn't he owe something on this day to his seamen? Some of them were mere lads a-hankering for home even as he. Yes, he had a duty. That evening he would break out a cask of beer, and invite all to drink, both planters and crew. He knew the forecastle hands would jolly well approve, and he had a hunch the planters wouldn't refuse.

He was right. They all "did drink cheerily together."

The planters pushed ahead with their building. Daily Christopher sent or went with the shallop to procure the fresh food so desperately needed. But days of driving

rain, sleet, snow, and wind hindered both operations. On some days three extra anchors were required to keep the pitching *Mayflower* from dragging ashore.

Then the Great Sickness came—sickness from cold, from too little food, "griefs" of the chest and the bones, the dread scurvy defying Dr. Heale's remedies. By the new year seven had died, and Christopher Martin was low unto death. He sent for John Carver to come on board to speak with him concerning his accounts. The epidemic invaded the forecastle, the 'tween deck, and the camp on shore in spite of careful sprinkling of vinegar and burning of tar, the preventives of the day.

Christopher renewed his efforts to procure food. He sent the shallop to more distant fishing grounds. It was fortunate his sailors had been with former fishing fleets. They brought back three great seals and an "excellent good cod which assured them they should have plenty of fish shortly."

The common house completed, it immediately became an infirmary as full of beds, mats on the hand-hewn plank floor, as they could lay one beside another. John Carver and William Bradford were among the sick. It was reported to Christopher that Bradford had asked for a little beer; and that the bosun had railed at him for asking, declaring, "If you were me own father you should have none." Christopher sent word to John Carver that those who needed beer should have it, though he drank water homeward bound.

On the weekend of January fourteen, since there were more passengers on shore than on ship, the planters asked that those on board be brought to the mainland for services in the common house. It would be the first time that all were together at their new home site.

Christopher wakened early. It was his job to get the group, mostly women and children, ashore. He listened to the wind whining in the rigging. The harbor would be rough going for shallop and longboat. Quickly dressing, he opened the cabin door. The sight that met his eyes— was it real or was he dreaming? The common house was ablaze. And in that wind. . . . The tide was out. Neither shallop nor longboat could go with help.

The alarm spread. Women and children crowded the ship's rail, some weeping loudly, others stunned into silence.

"Indians!" someone cried. "Indians have massacred our men and set fire to their house! Oh, that we had never come to America!"

And then the fire went out. Christopher shaded his eyes . . . the common house still stood . . . figures were running about. Were they friend or foe? It was difficult to tell at a mile and a half distance, but the figures looked like Englishmen to him.

Three quarters of an hour later, the tide was high enough to carry the loaded boats. With caution, Christopher approached the mainland until he could identify Elder Brewster, Captain Standish, and others who came to the rock to receive the passengers. The fire, he learned, had been caused by a spark that had caught in the thatch. No serious damage had been done, not even the roof boards burned. It had been hardest on the sick who were obliged to take up their loaded muskets and stagger or crawl outside.

During February the Great Sickness increased. Scarce were there enough well among them to care for the sick and bury the dead. The intrepid Elder Brewster and wiry Captain Standish seemed immune to the disease; they kept fires burning, cooked, and "cleansed the filth of sickness" for both seamen and landsmen. The tough old bosun confessed he did not deserve their kindness. In the end he died.

Christopher tramped the frozen forest that all might eat. The report of him on February the 9th is significant. "That evening, the master, going ashore, killed five geese, which he friendly distributed among the sick people."

Indians were becoming bolder; their campfires burned closer. From the *Mayflower,* Christopher saw two braves on Clark's Island intently studying the ship. One of the planters, a-fowling in tall reeds, saw twelve painted warriors march by. Others appeared on a hill and made signs to come to them, but when Captain Standish and Stephen Hopkins approached, they ran away. Tracks in the snow proved the planters were being watched from behind trees. Tools were stolen. It was high time the ordnance was mounted on the hill.

Over the ship's side, and into the shallop and long-boat, Christopher and sailors wrestled four cannon taken from the *Mayflower's* armament—two bases, a saker, and a minion. The guns were capable of firing iron balls, from a half to four pounds, up to seventeen hundred yards. On shore lay another piece which had been unloaded previously, making five cannon in all. Pulling together, seamen and planters tugged the cannon up the hill. No one objected to the sailors' heave-ho chanteys.

Mounted on the platform, ominous black barrels pointed in strategic directions. Captain Standish insisted on trying them out. Though the cannon kicked back furiously, knocking gunners off the platform if they didn't beware, the flashing artillery sent forth a deafening, earth-shaking, smoky challenge. "We'll see no more Indians for a time," predicted Captain Standish.

Work finished, Christopher brought from the shallop "a very fat goose" he had shot the evening before. The planters produced a fat crane, mallard, and dried neat's tongue. They ate and "were kindly and friendly together."

After the repast, John Carver beckoned Christopher aside. "Master Mullins is fast departing this life. He asks that we witness his will."

Up the single street that in the morning had been the scene of the cannon bout, went the two men, Plymouth governor and *Mayflower* captain. They paused before one of the finished cabins and knocked. Christopher noted the well-squared posts, the hand-sawed timbers standing on end, and the neat bundles of thatch. Son Joseph Mullins opened the door. Facing them in the single room was a cavernous fireplace built of board slabs and daubed with clay. In its mouth hung a black kettle which emitted a steamy medicinal smell.

Adjusting his eyes to the dimness of the interior, lit only by fireplace and one small window with pane of oiled paper, Christopher saw in the corner to the right of the fireplace a rustic hand-fashioned bed. On the bed, almost hidden by a rich English rug, lay the shoe merchant from Dorking, one of the first passengers to board the *Mayflower* in London. At the head of the bed stood

91

Mistress Mullins and daughter Priscilla silently weeping. Dr. Heale sat on a block of pine log, fingers on the sick man's pulse.

Too weak to write even his name, William Mullins haltingly told how his property and goods should be apportioned after his death. John Carver would later put the will into writing; the three witnesses would sign. The *Mayflower* would take the will to England where a relative would act as executor.

On the way back down the street, the men met a funeral procession. The planters buried their dead at night, smoothing over the graves that the Indians might not know how the colony was diminishing. On this day had died William White, Peregrine's father, and two others.

Wearily, Christopher climbed the *Mayflower's* ladder, lit a candle in the great cabin, opened the ship's log, and wrote February 21, 1621 at the top of the page. In a handwriting, decorated with sweeps and curls in spite of the tiredness of the hand that wrote, he recorded the events of the day. Record completed, he closed the book, wiped the quill with a sock that had long since lost heel and toe to the American wilderness, and frugally snuffed out the candle.

Tipping back in his chair Christopher relived the day. In the morning he had strained every muscle dragging the cannon up the hill. What must the Indians have thought when they heard the thunderous roar of the guns? And then there had been the dinner together. In the evening he had listened as a man spoke *last words* before entering eternity. He had promised to take those

words, William Mullins' last will and testament, to England when the *Mayflower* returned.

"When the *Mayflower* returned!" Would that day ever come? He recalled the funeral procession. If the Great Sickness didn't soon end, there would be no crew to sail her, no captain, no planters to tell the story. She would lie rotting in the harbor, a mute memorial to colonization, gulls roosting on her decks, until the teredo worms and storms did their complete work. And then she, too, would go to her grave.

Christopher brought his chair down with a bang. What hideous imaginings! A good night's sleep was what he needed. Tomorrow he would be taking on fish, not cannon. He kicked off his boots and got ready for bed.

March brought an early spring, and spring put winter and sickness to rout. Birds "sang pleasantly in the woods." Turkey cocks strutted in courtship. Buttercups yellowed the marshes here and there. Children pushed back the mat of leaves and grass to discover the first waxy pink blooms of arbutus. Women delved into the bottom of chests for bags of thyme, turnip, and parsnip seed they had brought from England.

The last family had moved from ship to shore. But the planters still clung to the *Mayflower* as a refuge against Indian attack. If only something would happen to give captain and ship a clear passport. Christopher knew that one day soon, passport or no, he would leave for home.

About noon of the twenty-third of March, returning from a longer than usual fishing trip, Christopher sailed the shallop toward the mainland to leave a part of his catch and to have a talk with Governor Carver about dismissing the ship. On the beach at the mouth of the brook he saw a strange sight. A man appeared to be dancing a jig. Had one of the planters lost his sanity? As he drew nearer he saw that the man was an Indian. The Indian looked up.

"Tisquantum! Where did you come from? What are you doing?"

Tisquantum stood his full height, crossed his arms, and grinned. Christopher listened as the Indian elaborated on his trip to America with Captain Dermer, and their map-making up and down the coast; and then he had come home. Tisquantum spread his arms wide. This land was his Patuxet. But when he had come he found his people were all dead—died of a great plague three summers before. Tisquantum dropped his arms, looked doleful, then brightened. Now that his white brothers from across the ocean had come to live at Patuxet, he had joined their tribe. Their governor would be his sachem, their God his Great Spirit. And just one sunrise ago, the white chief Carver and Massasoit, Indian king of the region, had made a treaty of peace. Now white men and red men would live peaceably together.

Tisquantum resumed his jigging. What was he doing? He was treading eels out of the mud. See the pile of fat ones? Would the captain like a sweet eel for his supper?

Christopher thanked Tisquantum, and hurried ashore to see John Carver, his thoughts racing. Now that Tisquantum had come, the planters would not lack for food. He would teach them the Indian way of trapping deer and catching cod. He would know where the berries and nuts grew; best of all he would teach them how to plant and grow the Indian corn.

And if it were true that a treaty had been signed between Indians and planters, and he had no reason to doubt Tisquantum, there would be no danger of attack. He would be free—*free to go home!*

11. The Thames Again

THE *Mayflower* stood out from Plymouth harbor a little before sunrise on April 5, 1621. She was half-manned, and carried her ensign at half-mast in honor of that half of her crew she was leaving behind buried under the waters or on the shore of the harbor. The gunner had been first to go, then the cook, the bosun, the carpenter . . .

All of the planters—they too, were but half of the original voyagers—were on the shore, Tisquantum with them, to see the good ship depart. With tears they said farewell to captain and mates. Christopher promised that he and the *Mayflower* would be back, come fall, to go whaling in the bay. Wordlessly, he and John Carver shook hands. Then the longboat crossed the distance between shore and ship for the last time.

Not one of those on land had sought passage back to England. Christopher was leaving with a new appreciation of the price men were willing to pay for freedom of worship. He had offered transportation to any woman who would act as cook on the return voyage. Only five of the original eighteen still lived—Mary Brewster, Elizabeth Hopkins, Ellen Billington, Catherine Carver, and Susanna White. The first three had brought their families through the dread winter intact. Who could say the sickness was a judgment of God, seeing that the Billingtons and Brewsters both survived.

Christopher had thought Susanna White might be glad to go, she with infant Peregrine less than three months and five-year-old Resolved clinging to her skirts, and her husband dead since February. Before she shook her head no, did he see a furtive glance pass between her and the scholarly Edward Winslow, now a widower?

Dr. Heale who had planned to stay was returning, but the ship's cooper, John Alden, who had planned to return was staying. The reason was apparent as he stood beside Priscilla Mullins, the maid who in the past few weeks had been bereft of father, mother, and brother. A substitute cooper would have to tend the ship's few remaining full casks.

As to cargo, the *Mayflower* carried bulging bags of mail, a bale of furs, and the bundle of eighteen arrows the Indians had shot at the planters that December morning of the third discovery—was it only four months ago? The ship carried stone for ballast. Provisions would be less than scanty, for the most part remnants of biscuit and beef from the voyage over, and dregs of beer. No vegetables, no lemons to combat scurvy.

The crew, though weak from recent illness, must work double watches at lines, yards, and helm, but they sang lustily. They were going home! Captain and mates would give a hand as needed.

The *Mayflower* made the turn of the Gurnet, blotting out the lingering group on shore. She passed by the arm of Cape Cod which at first had sheltered her and still beckoned. Finally, the heights of Truro—the first landmarks of the New World and where later Christopher and the planters dug up the baskets of corn—disappeared over the horizon.

The westerlies which had raged against the westward crossing now seemed to relent of former misdeeds and measured out a fair amount of wind to fill a ship's sails. In spite of her barnacle-encrusted hull, the *Mayflower* averaged four knots as she retraced the path she had made to New England. In no more than thirty days her familiar masts could be seen navigating the curves of the Thames. As in a dream Christopher tied up at London dock and saw his sailors go over the side to plunge into whatever excitement they could find—anything to forget the haunting memories of the long winter in Plymouth harbor. He was aware that "in seamen's hovels and in country cottages there would be more lamentation than rejoicing." Christopher stayed in London port only long enough to deliver the bags of mail to the post, the bundle of arrows and bale of furs to a disappointed Weston, and to place William Mullins' will with proper authorities. With a fresh crew he set sail for Harwich.

A thin fog gave him excuse to sound ship's trumpet as he entered Harwich harbor. That Josian would hear, he was certain. He donned his going-ashore clothes, and then wished he hadn't. They hung on him like sacks.

The *Mayflower's* trumpet had been heard. Thomas and Roger were on the wharf to watch her come in. How they had grown in his ten months' absence! Only when they looked beyond him as if looking for someone else, did Christopher realize how much *he* must have changed. When he spoke they laughed at their mistake. Together they walked up the narrow street to the stone house on the Stour, questions and answers tumbling over each other. Joane and Grace came running to meet them, each claiming a father's hand.

Josian waited in the doorway. Christopher saw an instant of horror cross her face which she quickly erased with a forced smile. "It has been so long, Christopher," she said.

He kissed her hand, a custom he had always observed —"the most beautiful custom in all England," Josian had stoutly declared when a small girl—before taking her in his arms. The embrace was interrupted by a chortling and squealing. The youngest member of the Jones family was coming to welcome his father, propelled by all four oars. Skipper Jon had learned to crawl.

Christopher moved his family back to Rotherhithe. Josian stewed, brewed, and did everything she knew or the neighbors suggested to get her husband back to his once rugged self. That she partially succeeded, a port entry dated October 31, 1621 testifies. On that date Captain Christopher Jones and the *Mayflower* unloaded a cargo of bay salt from Rochelle, France on a London dock. From there on port entries are silent. Church records take up the story.

On the fifth of March (1622), Josian and the children —Roger, Joane, Grace, and Thomas carrying Skipper Jon—followed Christopher's bier to St. Mary's churchyard. The stay in New England had been too long. The Great Sickness had followed him home. While the church bell solemnly tolled fifty-two, they buried him beside that other Christopher who had hardly lived at all. The small grave, the large grave—because they were side by side, neither seemed quite alone.

Next morning, Josian, not realizing she was repeating the words of another woman some forty-odd years before, said to her eldest son, "Thomas, beginning today, you will sit at your father's place. You are now ye head of our family."

APPENDIX

The signature of Captain Christopher
Jones, written in Old English script and
spelling, as it appears on the will of
William Mullins, the first will ever made
in New England. *From the copy in the
Massachusetts Historical Society.*

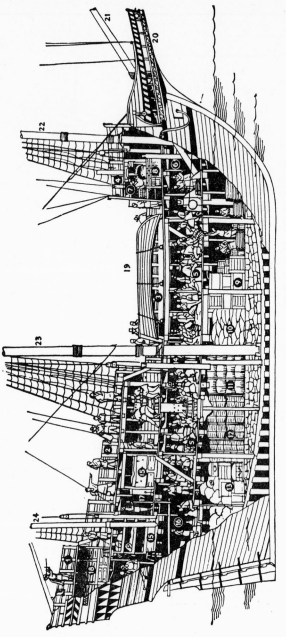

A CUTAWAY DRAWING OF THE *MAYFLOWER*

1-Poop deck. 2-Quarter-deck. 3-Upper deck. 4-Fore-castle. 5-Main deck. 6-Crew quarters. 7-Bosun's store. 8-Galley. 9-13-Hold, with food and supplies. 14-Typical temporary cabin. 15-Special cabins. 16-Tiller room. 17-Helmsman; whipstaff connects to tiller. 18-Captain's "Great Room." 19-Longboat. 20-Beak. 21-Bowsprit. 22-Foremast. 23-Mainmast. 24-Mizzenmast. *Courtesy of Plimoth Plantation.*

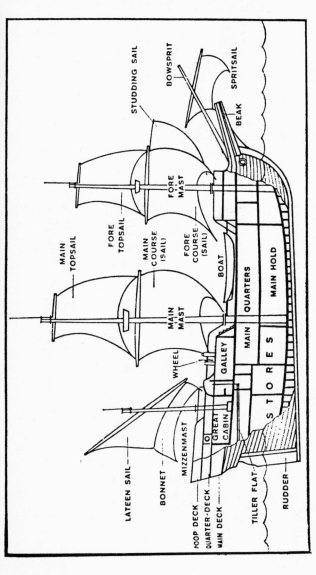

Cutaway View of *Mayflower II,* patterned after *Mayflower I* but with two exceptions: *Mayflower I* did not have the indicated galley and was steered with a whipstaff instead of a wheel. *From Life Magazine,* © *1957 Time Inc. Used by permission.*

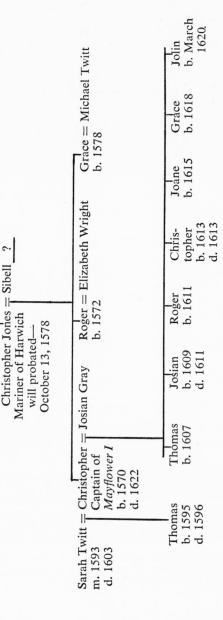

Genealogical chart showing the known ancestry and descendants of Captain Christopher Jones.

SELECTIVE BIBLIOGRAPHY

If you wish to read more about—

CHRISTOPHER JONES:

> *The Master of the Mayflower* (1936) by Henry Justin Smith. (You may have to borrow the book through inter-library loan, but it is the best.)

> "The *Mayflower*" by R. G. Marsden in the *English Historical Review,* Vol. 19: 669-80, October 1904, in which Mr. Marsden explodes the myth that the captain of the *Mayflower* was the pirate, Thomas Jones (p. 672.)

> "The *Mayflower's* Jones" by Gershom Bradford in *The American Neptune,* Vol. 17: 128-33, April 1957. (Contains refutation of bribery charge and enumerates the captain's many kindnesses during the long winter in Plymouth.)

THE MAYFLOWER:

> *Land Ho!—1620* (1931) by Captain W. Sears Nickerson.

> "The *Mayflower,* Her Identity and Tonnage" by J. R. Hutchinson in the *New England Historical and Genealogical Register,* Vol. 70: 337-42, in which Mr. Hutchinson quotes London Port Books.

Selective Bibliography

"A *Mayflower* Model" by R. C. Anderson in *Mariner's Mirror,* Vol. 12: 260-262, July 1926.

"Mayflower Officers and Crew" by Charles E. Banks in *Massachusetts Historical Society,* Vol. 60: 210-21, April 1927.

"The 66-Day Saga of *Mayflower I"* by S. E. Morison in *New York Times Magazine,* April 14, 1957, p. 12.

THE PILGRIMS:

Mourt's Relation (1622) "Writ by the several actors (Pilgrims) themselves." The most readable edition with modern spelling, punctuation, and paragraphing, the original text intact, is edited by Dwight B. Heath under the title *A Journal of the Pilgrims at Plymouth* (1963).

Of Plimoth Plantation (General Court Edition, 1899) by William Bradford. Next to *Mourt's Relation* perhaps the most valuable source for research—a first person account written from memory many years after the voyage, but unfortunately with a personal prejudice against seamen.

The Story of the "Old Colony" of New Plymouth (1956) by Samuel Eliot Morison.

Western Star (1943) by Stephen Vincent Benét, pp. 119-51 (a poem and a must).

History and Genealogy of the Mayflower Planters and First Comers to Ye Old Colonie (1936) by Leon Clark Hills.

Arms & Armor of the Pilgrims (1957) by Harold L. Petersen, obtainable through Plimoth Plantation or Pilgrim Hall, Plymouth, Mass.

Selective Bibliography

The English Ancestry and Homes of the Pilgrim Fathers (1929) by Charles Edward Banks.

Mayflower Heroes (1931) by Gleason L. Archer.

Saints and Strangers (1946) by George Willison.

The England and Holland of the Pilgrims (1905) by Henry Martyn Dexter.

The Story of the Pilgrim Fathers, 1606-1623 A.D.; *as told by Themselves, Their Friends, and Their Enemies* (1897) by Edward Arber.

TISQUANTUM:

Three Episodes of Massachusetts History (1892) by Charles Francis Adams, Vol. 1: 23-44.

Dictionary of American Biography, Vol. XVII, p. 487.

THE WILL OF WILLIAM MULLINS:

Massachusetts Historical Society, February 1927.

"The Will of William Mullins" with notes by George Ernest Bowman, *The Mayflower Descendant,* Vol. 1: 230-32.

SHALLOP:

"Notes on a Shallop" by William A. Baker in *The American Neptune,* Vol. 17: 105-13, April 1957. (Sketch of shallop).

CUSTOMS OF ELIZABETHAN AND STUART ENGLAND:

The Elizabethans at Home (1958) by Elizabeth Burton.

Life in Elizabethan Days (1930) by William Stearns Davis.

109

Selective Bibliography

An Elizabethan Song Book (1955) by Noah Greenberg, W. H. Auden, and Chester Kallman.

The Ainsworth Psalms (Hymnal used by the Pilgrims). Rare book rooms only.

Social Life in Stuart England (1924) by Mary Coate.

The Streets of London through the Centuries (1940) by Thomas Burke.

MAYFLOWER II:

The New Mayflower: Her Design and Construction (1958) by William A. Baker, Barre, Mass.: Barre *Gazette* (includes envelope of large-size, detailed plans).

"We're Coming Over on the *Mayflower*" by Captain Alan Villiers in the *National Geographic Magazine,* Vol. 111: 708-28, May 1957.

"How We Sailed the New *Mayflower* to America" by Captain Alan Villiers in the *National Geographic Magazine,* Vol. 112: 627-72, November 1957.

"Sailing Westward with a Cargo of History" by Maitland A. Edey and Gordon Tenney in *Life,* Vol. 42: 62, May 13, 1957.

"A Tale of Stout Men and a Good Ship on a Modern Pilgrimage" by Maitland A. Edey and Gordon Tenney in *Life,* Vol. 42: 20. June 17, 1957.

"A 20th-Century Saga of the Sea on Canvas" by Hervey Garrett Smith in the *National Geographic Magazine,* Vol. 112: 673-4, September 1957. (Excellent reproduction of oil painting of *Mayflower II* in Supplement).

Related Historical Events—

VOYAGES OF SIR MARTIN FROBISHER:

Voyages of the Elizabethan Seamen to America, selected narratives from the "Principle Navigations" of Hakluyt, edited (1893) by Edward John Payne.

The Three Voyages of Martin Frobisher in Search of a Passage to Cathay and India by the North-West (1578) by George Best, edited (1938) by Vilhjámur Stefánsson and Eloise McCaskill.

Elizabethan Seamen (1936) by Douglas Herbert Bell. (Accounts of Frobisher, Armada, and the *Madre de Dios* episode.)

THE SPANISH ARMADA:

Elizabethan Sea-Dogs (1918) by William Wood, pp. 172-191.

The Spanish Armada, state papers relating to the defeat of ——, edited by John Knox Laughton, London. Printed for the Navy Records Society, 1894. (List of Queen's ships and men, pp. 324-31.)

The Armada (1959) by Garrett Mattingly. Title of London edition, *The Defeat of the Spanish Armada.*

MADRE DE DIOS:

Hakluyt's Voyages by Richard Hakluyt (the 1904 edition in 12 volumes) Vol. 7: 105-118.

Naval Tracts of Sir William Monson (1902-14) printed for the Navy Records Society, London, Vol. 1: 278-96.

SAILING SQUARE-RIGGER SHIPS:

Admiral of the Ocean Sea (1942) Vol. 1, by Samuel Eliot Morison. (Mr. Morison explains sailing square-rigger ships in a way that a landsman can understand.)

Ships and Ways of Other Days (1913) by E. Keble Chatterton.

Ships and Sailors (1928) by Stanley Reginald Rogers.

A History of the Merchant Navy (1937) by H. Moyse-Bartlett.

Travels and Works of Captain John Smith, as edited by Edward Arber (1910) pp. 789-804, "Accidence, or Pathway to Experience for Young Seamen."

"The Way of a Ship" by L. G. Carr Laughton in *Mariner's Mirror,* Vol. 14: 132-48, April 1928.